2017 - 2018

JULY 2017

S	M	T	W	T	F	S
						1
2	3	4	5	6	7	8
9	10	11	12	13	14	15
16	17	18	19	20	21	22
23	24	25	26	27	28	29
30	31					

AUGUST 2017

S	M	T	W	T	F	S
		1	2	3	4	5
6	7	8	9	10	11	12
13	14	15	16	17	18	19
20	21	22	23	24	25	26
27	28	29	30	31		

SEPTEMBER 2

S	M	T	W	T	F	S
					1	2
3	4	5	6	7	8	9
10	11	12	13	14	15	16
17	18	19	20	21	22	23
24	25	26	27	28	29	30

1	2	3	4	5	6	7
8	9	10	11	12	13	14
15	16	17	18	19	20	21
22	23	24	25	26	27	28
29	30	31				

NOVEMBER 2017

S	M	T	W	T	F	S
			1	2	3	4
5	6	7	8	9	10	11
12	13	14	15	16	17	18
19	20	21	22	23	24	25
26	27	28	29	30		

DECEMBER 2017

S	M	T	W	T	F	S
					1	2
3	4	5	6	7	8	9
10	11	12	13	14	15	16
17	18	19	20	21	22	23
24	25	26	27	28	29	30
31						

JANUARY 2018

S	M	T	W	T	F	S
	1	2	3	4	5	6
7	8	9	10	11	12	13
14	15	16	17	18	19	20
21	22	23	24	25	26	27
28	29	30	31			

FEBRUARY 2018

S	M	T	W	T	F	S
				1	2	3
4	5	6	7	8	9	10
11	12	13	14	15	16	17
18	19	20	21	22	23	24
25	26	27	28			

MARCH 2018

S	M	T	W	T	F	S
				1	2	3
4	5	6	7	8	9	10
11	12	13	14	15	16	17
18	19	20	21	22	23	24
25	26	27	28	29	30	31

APRIL 2018

S	M	T	W	T	F	S
1	2	3	4	5	6	7
8	9	10	11	12	13	14
15	16	17	18	19	20	21
22	23	24	25	26	27	28
29	30					

MAY 2018

S	M	T	W	T	F	S
		1	2	3	4	5
6	7	8	9	10	11	12
13	14	15	16	17	18	19
20	21	22	23	24	25	26
27	28	29	30	31		

JUNE 2018

S	M	T	W	T	F	S
					1	2
3	4	5	6	7	8	9
10	11	12	13	14	15	16
17	18	19	20	21	22	23
24	25	26	27	28	29	30

2018 - 2019

JULY 2018

S	M	T	W	T	F	S
1	2	3	4	5	6	7
8	9	10	11	12	13	14
15	16	17	18	19	20	21
22	23	24	25	26	27	28
29	30	31				

AUGUST 2018

S	M	T	W	T	F	S
			1	2	3	4
5	6	7	8	9	10	11
12	13	14	15	16	17	18
19	20	21	22	23	24	25
26	27	28	29	30	31	

SEPTEMBER 2018

S	M	T	W	T	F	S
						1
2	3	4	5	6	7	8
9	10	11	12	13	14	15
16	17	18	19	20	21	22
23	24	25	26	27	28	29
30						

OCTOBER 2018

S	M	T	W	T	F	S
	1	2	3	4	5	6
7	8	9	10	11	12	13
14	15	16	17	18	19	20
21	22	23	24	25	26	27
28	29	30	31			

NOVEMBER 2018

S	M	T	W	T	F	S
				1	2	3
4	5	6	7	8	9	10
11	12	13	14	15	16	17
18	19	20	21	22	23	24
25	26	27	28	29	30	

DECEMBER 2018

S	M	T	W	T	F	S
						1
2	3	4	5	6	7	8
9	10	11	12	13	14	15
16	17	18	19	20	21	22
23	24	25	26	27	28	29
30	31					

JANUARY 2019

S	M	T	W	T	F	S
		1	2	3	4	5
6	7	8	9	10	11	12
13	14	15	16	17	18	19
20	21	22	23	24	25	26
27	28	29	30	31		

FEBRUARY 2019

S	M	T	W	T	F	S
					1	2
3	4	5	6	7	8	9
10	11	12	13	14	15	16
17	18	19	20	21	22	23
24	25	26	27	28		

MARCH 2019

S	M	T	W	T	F	S
					1	2
3	4	5	6	7	8	9
10	11	12	13	14	15	16
17	18	19	20	21	22	23
24	25	26	27	28	29	30
31						

APRIL 2019

S	M	T	W	T	F	S
	1	2	3	4	5	6
7	8	9	10	11	12	13
14	15	16	17	18	19	20
21	22	23	24	25	26	27
28	29	30				

MAY 2019

S	M	T	W	T	F	S
			1	2	3	4
5	6	7	8	9	10	11
12	13	14	15	16	17	18
19	20	21	22	23	24	25
26	27	28	29	30	31	

JUNE 2019

S	M	T	W	T	F	S
						1
2	3	4	5	6	7	8
9	10	11	12	13	14	15
16	17	18	19	20	21	22
23	24	25	26	27	28	29
30						

2019 - 2020

JULY 2019

S	M	T	W	T	F	S
	1	2	3	4	5	6
7	8	9	10	11	12	13
14	15	16	17	18	19	20
21	22	23	24	25	26	27
28	29	30	31			

AUGUST 2019

S	M	T	W	T	F	S
				1	2	3
4	5	6	7	8	9	10
11	12	13	14	15	16	17
18	19	20	21	22	23	24
25	26	27	28	29	30	31

SEPTEMBER 2019

S	M	T	W	T	F	S
1	2	3	4	5	6	7
8	9	10	11	12	13	14
15	16	17	18	19	20	21
22	23	24	25	26	27	28
29	30					

OCTOBER 2019

S	M	T	W	T	F	S
		1	2	3	4	5
6	7	8	9	10	11	12
13	14	15	16	17	18	19
20	21	22	23	24	25	26
27	28	29	30	31		

NOVEMBER 2019

S	M	T	W	T	F	S
					1	2
3	4	5	6	7	8	9
10	11	12	13	14	15	16
17	18	19	20	21	22	23
24	25	26	27	28	29	30

DECEMBER 2019

S	M	T	W	T	F	S
1	2	3	4	5	6	7
8	9	10	11	12	13	14
15	16	17	18	19	20	21
22	23	24	25	26	27	28
29	30	31				

JANUARY 2020

S	M	T	W	T	F	S
			1	2	3	4
5	6	7	8	9	10	11
12	13	14	15	16	17	18
19	20	21	22	23	24	25
26	27	28	29	30	31	

FEBRUARY 2020

S	M	T	W	T	F	S
						1
2	3	4	5	6	7	8
9	10	11	12	13	14	15
16	17	18	19	20	21	22
23	24	25	26	27	28	29

MARCH 2020

S	M	T	W	T	F	S
1	2	3	4	5	6	7
8	9	10	11	12	13	14
15	16	17	18	19	20	21
22	23	24	25	26	27	28
29	30	31				

APRIL 2020

S	M	T	W	T	F	S
			1	2	3	4
5	6	7	8	9	10	11
12	13	14	15	16	17	18
19	20	21	22	23	24	25
26	27	28	29	30		

MAY 2020

S	M	T	W	T	F	S
					1	2
3	4	5	6	7	8	9
10	11	12	13	14	15	16
17	18	19	20	21	22	23
24	25	26	27	28	29	30
31						

JUNE 2020

S	M	T	W	T	F	S
	1	2	3	4	5	6
7	8	9	10	11	12	13
14	15	16	17	18	19	20
21	22	23	24	25	26	27
28	29	30				

2020 - 2021

JULY 2020

S	M	T	W	T	F	S
			1	2	3	4
5	6	7	8	9	10	11
12	13	14	15	16	17	18
19	20	21	22	23	24	25
26	27	28	29	30	31	

AUGUST 2020

S	M	T	W	T	F	S
						1
2	3	4	5	6	7	8
9	10	11	12	13	14	15
16	17	18	19	20	21	22
23	24	25	26	27	28	29
30	31					

SEPTEMBER 2020

S	M	T	W	T	F	S
		1	2	3	4	5
6	7	8	9	10	11	12
13	14	15	16	17	18	19
20	21	22	23	24	25	26
27	28	29	30			

OCTOBER 2020

S	M	T	W	T	F	S
				1	2	3
4	5	6	7	8	9	10
11	12	13	14	15	16	17
18	19	20	21	22	23	24
25	26	27	28	29	30	31

NOVEMBER 2020

S	M	T	W	T	F	S
1	2	3	4	5	6	7
8	9	10	11	12	13	14
15	16	17	18	19	20	21
22	23	24	25	26	27	28
29	30					

DECEMBER 2020

S	M	T	W	T	F	S
		1	2	3	4	5
6	7	8	9	10	11	12
13	14	15	16	17	18	19
20	21	22	23	24	25	26
27	28	29	30	31		

JANUARY 2021

S	M	T	W	T	F	S
					1	2
3	4	5	6	7	8	9
10	11	12	13	14	15	16
17	18	19	20	21	22	23
24	25	26	27	28	29	30
31						

FEBRUARY 2021

S	M	T	W	T	F	S
	1	2	3	4	5	6
7	8	9	10	11	12	13
14	15	16	17	18	19	20
21	22	23	24	25	26	27
28						

MARCH 2021

S	M	T	W	T	F	S
	1	2	3	4	5	6
7	8	9	10	11	12	13
14	15	16	17	18	19	20
21	22	23	24	25	26	27
28	29	30	31			

APRIL 2021

S	M	T	W	T	F	S
				1	2	3
4	5	6	7	8	9	10
11	12	13	14	15	16	17
18	19	20	21	22	23	24
25	26	27	28	29	30	

MAY 2021

S	M	T	W	T	F	S
						1
2	3	4	5	6	7	8
9	10	11	12	13	14	15
16	17	18	19	20	21	22
23	24	25	26	27	28	29
30	31					

JUNE 2021

S	M	T	W	T	F	S
		1	2	3	4	5
6	7	8	9	10	11	12
13	14	15	16	17	18	19
20	21	22	23	24	25	26
27	28	29	30			

2021 - 2022

JULY 2021

S	M	T	W	T	F	S
				1	2	3
4	5	6	7	8	9	10
11	12	13	14	15	16	17
18	19	20	21	22	23	24
25	26	27	28	29	30	31

AUGUST 2021

S	M	T	W	T	F	S
1	2	3	4	5	6	7
8	9	10	11	12	13	14
15	16	17	18	19	20	21
22	23	24	25	26	27	28
29	30	31				

SEPTEMBER 2021

S	M	T	W	T	F	S
			1	2	3	4
5	6	7	8	9	10	11
12	13	14	15	16	17	18
19	20	21	22	23	24	25
26	27	28	29	30		

OCTOBER 2021

S	M	T	W	T	F	S
					1	2
3	4	5	6	7	8	9
10	11	12	13	14	15	16
17	18	19	20	21	22	23
24	25	26	27	28	29	30
31						

NOVEMBER 2021

S	M	T	W	T	F	S
	1	2	3	4	5	6
7	8	9	10	11	12	13
14	15	16	17	18	19	20
21	22	23	24	25	26	27
28	29	30				

DECEMBER 2021

S	M	T	W	T	F	S
			1	2	3	4
5	6	7	8	9	10	11
12	13	14	15	16	17	18
19	20	21	22	23	24	25
26	27	28	29	30	31	

JANUARY 2022

S	M	T	W	T	F	S
						1
2	3	4	5	6	7	8
9	10	11	12	13	14	15
16	17	18	19	20	21	22
23	24	25	26	27	28	29
30	31					

FEBRUARY 2022

S	M	T	W	T	F	S
		1	2	3	4	5
6	7	8	9	10	11	12
13	14	15	16	17	18	19
20	21	22	23	24	25	26
27	28					

MARCH 2022

S	M	T	W	T	F	S
		1	2	3	4	5
6	7	8	9	10	11	12
13	14	15	16	17	18	19
20	21	22	23	24	25	26
27	28	29	30	31		

APRIL 2022

S	M	T	W	T	F	S
					1	2
3	4	5	6	7	8	9
10	11	12	13	14	15	16
17	18	19	20	21	22	23
24	25	26	27	28	29	30

MAY 2022

S	M	T	W	T	F	S
1	2	3	4	5	6	7
8	9	10	11	12	13	14
15	16	17	18	19	20	21
22	23	24	25	26	27	28
29	30	31				

JUNE 2022

S	M	T	W	T	F	S
			1	2	3	4
5	6	7	8	9	10	11
12	13	14	15	16	17	18
19	20	21	22	23	24	25
26	27	28	29	30		

2022 - 2023

JULY 2022

S	M	T	W	T	F	S
					1	2
3	4	5	6	7	8	9
10	11	12	13	14	15	16
17	18	19	20	21	22	23
24	25	26	27	28	29	30
31						

AUGUST 2022

S	M	T	W	T	F	S
	1	2	3	4	5	6
7	8	9	10	11	12	13
14	15	16	17	18	19	20
21	22	23	24	25	26	27
28	29	30	31			

SEPTEMBER 2022

S	M	T	W	T	F	S
				1	2	3
4	5	6	7	8	9	10
11	12	13	14	15	16	17
18	19	20	21	22	23	24
25	26	27	28	29	30	

OCTOBER 2022

S	M	T	W	T	F	S
						1
2	3	4	5	6	7	8
9	10	11	12	13	14	15
16	17	18	19	20	21	22
23	24	25	26	27	28	29
30	31					

NOVEMBER 2022

S	M	T	W	T	F	S
		1	2	3	4	5
6	7	8	9	10	11	12
13	14	15	16	17	18	19
20	21	22	23	24	25	26
27	28	29	30			

DECEMBER 2022

S	M	T	W	T	F	S
				1	2	3
4	5	6	7	8	9	10
11	12	13	14	15	16	17
18	19	20	21	22	23	24
25	26	27	28	29	30	31

JANUARY 2023

S	M	T	W	T	F	S
1	2	3	4	5	6	7
8	9	10	11	12	13	14
15	16	17	18	19	20	21
22	23	24	25	26	27	28
29	30	31				

FEBRUARY 2023

S	M	T	W	T	F	S
			1	2	3	4
5	6	7	8	9	10	11
12	13	14	15	16	17	18
19	20	21	22	23	24	25
26	27	28				

MARCH 2023

S	M	T	W	T	F	S
			1	2	3	4
5	6	7	8	9	10	11
12	13	14	15	16	17	18
19	20	21	22	23	24	25
26	27	28	29	30	31	

APRIL 2023

S	M	T	W	T	F	S
						1
2	3	4	5	6	7	8
9	10	11	12	13	14	15
16	17	18	19	20	21	22
23	24	25	26	27	28	29
30						

MAY 2023

S	M	T	W	T	F	S
	1	2	3	4	5	6
7	8	9	10	11	12	13
14	15	16	17	18	19	20
21	22	23	24	25	26	27
28	29	30	31			

JUNE 2023

S	M	T	W	T	F	S
				1	2	3
4	5	6	7	8	9	10
11	12	13	14	15	16	17
18	19	20	21	22	23	24
25	26	27	28	29	30	

2023 - 2024

JULY 2023

S	M	T	W	T	F	S
						1
2	3	4	5	6	7	8
9	10	11	12	13	14	15
16	17	18	19	20	21	22
23	24	25	26	27	28	29
30	31					

AUGUST 2023

S	M	T	W	T	F	S
		1	2	3	4	5
6	7	8	9	10	11	12
13	14	15	16	17	18	19
20	21	22	23	24	25	26
27	28	29	30	31		

SEPTEMBER 2023

S	M	T	W	T	F	S
					1	2
3	4	5	6	7	8	9
10	11	12	13	14	15	16
17	18	19	20	21	22	23
24	25	26	27	28	29	30

OCTOBER 2023

S	M	T	W	T	F	S
1	2	3	4	5	6	7
8	9	10	11	12	13	14
15	16	17	18	19	20	21
22	23	24	25	26	27	28
29	30	31				

NOVEMBER 2023

S	M	T	W	T	F	S
			1	2	3	4
5	6	7	8	9	10	11
12	13	14	15	16	17	18
19	20	21	22	23	24	25
26	27	28	29	30		

DECEMBER 2023

S	M	T	W	T	F	S
					1	2
3	4	5	6	7	8	9
10	11	12	13	14	15	16
17	18	19	20	21	22	23
24	25	26	27	28	29	30
31						

JANUARY 2024

S	M	T	W	T	F	S
	1	2	3	4	5	6
7	8	9	10	11	12	13
14	15	16	17	18	19	20
21	22	23	24	25	26	27
28	29	30	31			

FEBRUARY 2024

S	M	T	W	T	F	S
				1	2	3
4	5	6	7	8	9	10
11	12	13	14	15	16	17
18	19	20	21	22	23	24
25	26	27	28	29		

MARCH 2024

S	M	T	W	T	F	S
					1	2
3	4	5	6	7	8	9
10	11	12	13	14	15	16
17	18	19	20	21	22	23
24	25	26	27	28	29	30
31						

APRIL 2024

S	M	T	W	T	F	S
	1	2	3	4	5	6
7	8	9	10	11	12	13
14	15	16	17	18	19	20
21	22	23	24	25	26	27
28	29	30				

MAY 2024

S	M	T	W	T	F	S
			1	2	3	4
5	6	7	8	9	10	11
12	13	14	15	16	17	18
19	20	21	22	23	24	25
26	27	28	29	30	31	

JUNE 2024

S	M	T	W	T	F	S
						1
2	3	4	5	6	7	8
9	10	11	12	13	14	15
16	17	18	19	20	21	22
23	24	25	26	27	28	29
30						

2024 - 2025

JULY 2024

S	M	T	W	T	F	S
	1	2	3	4	5	6
7	8	9	10	11	12	13
14	15	16	17	18	19	20
21	22	23	24	25	26	27
28	29	30	31			

AUGUST 2024

S	M	T	W	T	F	S
				1	2	3
4	5	6	7	8	9	10
11	12	13	14	15	16	17
18	19	20	21	22	23	24
25	26	27	28	29	30	31

SEPTEMBER 2024

S	M	T	W	T	F	S
1	2	3	4	5	6	7
8	9	10	11	12	13	14
15	16	17	18	19	20	21
22	23	24	25	26	27	28
29	30					

OCTOBER 2024

S	M	T	W	T	F	S
		1	2	3	4	5
6	7	8	9	10	11	12
13	14	15	16	17	18	19
20	21	22	23	24	25	26
27	28	29	30	31		

NOVEMBER 2024

S	M	T	W	T	F	S
					1	2
3	4	5	6	7	8	9
10	11	12	13	14	15	16
17	18	19	20	21	22	23
24	25	26	27	28	29	30

DECEMBER 2024

S	M	T	W	T	F	S
1	2	3	4	5	6	7
8	9	10	11	12	13	14
15	16	17	18	19	20	21
22	23	24	25	26	27	28
29	30	31				

JANUARY 2025

S	M	T	W	T	F	S
			1	2	3	4
5	6	7	8	9	10	11
12	13	14	15	16	17	18
19	20	21	22	23	24	25
26	27	28	29	30	31	

FEBRUARY 2025

S	M	T	W	T	F	S
						1
2	3	4	5	6	7	8
9	10	11	12	13	14	15
16	17	18	19	20	21	22
23	24	25	26	27	28	

MARCH 2025

S	M	T	W	T	F	S
						1
2	3	4	5	6	7	8
9	10	11	12	13	14	15
16	17	18	19	20	21	22
23	24	25	26	27	28	29
30	31					

APRIL 2025

S	M	T	W	T	F	S
		1	2	3	4	5
6	7	8	9	10	11	12
13	14	15	16	17	18	19
20	21	22	23	24	25	26
27	28	29	30			

MAY 2025

S	M	T	W	T	F	S
				1	2	3
4	5	6	7	8	9	10
11	12	13	14	15	16	17
18	19	20	21	22	23	24
25	26	27	28	29	30	31

JUNE 2025

S	M	T	W	T	F	S
1	2	3	4	5	6	7
8	9	10	11	12	13	14
15	16	17	18	19	20	21
22	23	24	25	26	27	28
29	30					

The Ultimate Homeschool Planner

a planning system designed by

Debra Bell

count your **blessings** encourage **independence** record your **progress**

School Year:	
Name:	
Address:	
Phone Number:	E-mail:
Students:	Grades:

"Order brings peace."
– St. Augustine (traditional)

The Ultimate Homeschool Planner

Published by
Apologia Educational Ministries, Inc.
1106 Meridian Street, Suite 340
Anderson, Indiana 46016
www.apologia.com

Manufactured in South Korea
Fifth Printing: April 2018

Yellow Cover ISBN: 978-1-935495-65-9
Purple Cover ISBN: 978-1-935495-93-2

Cover and design by Doug Powell
Managing Editor: Zan Tyler

Printed by Asia Printing Co., Ltd, Seoul, South Korea

apologia

The Ultimate Homeschool Planning System consists of three parts:

The Ultimate Homeschool Planner
(for moms)

The Ultimate Weekly Planner for Teens
(for 7th–12th graders)

The Ultimate Daily Planner for Students
(for 4th–8th graders)

The Ultimate Homeschool Planner could be used alone, but the entire system is designed to work together so that your students gradually take on more and more responsibility for their own planning and scheduling. Ideally, the mom should have *The Ultimate Homeschool Planner* and each student should have his or her own planner.

Welcome to The Ultimate Homeschool Planning System

As experienced homeschool moms, we feel your pain. We remember the little things that brought the house down, and we know what made our lives easier. That's why we worked together to create this planning system to make *your* life easier. (Zan came up with the concept, and Debra designed the system.)

Planning won't eliminate chaos and disorder, but it can reduce it. Planning won't remove frustration, but it can help you stave off burnout. Flying by the seat of your pants is an exhausting approach. Taking thirty minutes a week to find a quiet place and sketch out a high-level view of the week ahead is going to give you peace of mind. Planning at monthly and yearly intervals will ensure you hit the targets you were shooting for when you decided to homeschool in the first place.

"Order brings peace" is a traditional saying often attributed to St. Augustine. If it was true then, it is even more relevant in our modern culture. We rush through time and space, often at breakneck speed and with no clear destination in view. If you don't make time to plan, then you'll find that you, your kids, your homeschool, and your parenting years will be dragged down by the undertow. We want you to do more than just survive your call to homeschool; we want you to thrive in the pleasure of God's calling on your life.

In addition to helping you as the teacher, The Ultimate Homeschool Planning System is designed to teach your student to be an independent learner. Training your children to work independently won't guarantee smooth sailing all the way, but it will give you the navigational skills necessary to steer a course toward your most important destination—raising up mature, responsible adults equipped to fulfill God's call upon their own lives. This will enable you to focus more time and attention on your little ones while your older kids incrementally take on more and more ownership and initiative in managing their time, tracking their achievements, and setting their goals.

Ultimately, It's God's Story

Practicalities aside, the burning desire of our hearts is that you experience a greater awareness of God's activity in your homeschool journey. Homeschooling is not a cross to bear—rather it's an opportunity to experience God's grace, God's faithfulness, God's mercy, God's provision, and God's redemptive activity in your own life, in each of your kids' lives, and in your family life.

This is the most important documentation you can keep about your homeschooling years. It's what your kids will want to remember; it's what your grandchildren will want to hear about. God is faithful from generation to generation.

Herein is recorded how He was particularly faithful—*this* year, to *this* family. And with the psalmist, we can declare, "I will remember the deeds of the Lord; yes, I will remember your miracles of long ago" (Psalm 77:11).

Soli Deo Gloria,

Debra Zan

Debra Bell & Zan Tyler

Table of Contents

HOW TO USE THE ULTIMATE HOMESCHOOL PLANNING SYSTEM

Stephen R. Covey tells the following story in his book *First Things First*. It has since been retold many, many times. Here's my version of it:

One day a business professor set a wide-mouth Mason jar on the table in front of his students. First he filled the jar with large rocks and asked his rising business managers if the jar was full. "Yes?" they queried.

From under the table, he took a bag of stones and dumped these in the jar. "Is the jar full now?" he asked. "No!" they replied, catching on quickly. Next he dumped in a scoopful of sand. "Is it filled now?" "No!" they exclaimed. Finally he poured a glass of water into the jar, filling it to the brim.

"What have we learned from this illustration?" he asked. "That we can always fit more into our day if we try?" one student suggested. "No," said the professor. "The lesson is this: if you don't put the big rocks in the jar of life first, you won't get them in at all."

Enjoy a God-Ordered LIfe

In His great prayer to the Father, Jesus said, "I have brought you glory on earth by completing the work you gave me to do" (John 17:4). Likewise, we are called to a God-ordered life. This planner is designed to help you prayerfully prioritize the big rocks in your family's jar of life and to glorify God by completing the work He has called you to.

There will always be more to do in homeschooling than you have time to do. And that's a God-designed tension. It will cause you to depend upon His faithfulness, not your own. God is active in your family! And He is the only one who makes things grow (1 Corinthians 3:7). We are called to draw attention to that reality.

Plan for Peace and Guide Your Kids toward Independence

The Ultimate Homeschool Planning System recommends five painless steps to guide you in the process:

1. A yearly planning retreat (4–8 hours)
2. Monthly planning sessions (2 hours)
3. Weekly planning breaks (30 minutes)
4. Monday morning tutorials (20 minutes per child)
5. Friday afternoon weekly reviews (15 minutes per child)

Establish a Yearly Planning Retreat (4–8 hours)

Tools:

- One-Year Planning Grid (pages 18-19)
- Student Goal Setter (pages 20-21)
- Family Priorities form (page 22)

Purpose:

- Set academic and character goals for each child.
- Prioritize those goals at the family level.

Before heading off for your yearly planning retreat (I went to the local library for the day), review the preceding school year with your kids. Find out what they liked, what they didn't like, and what goals they have for the year ahead. Ask what their suggestions are for what they'd like to learn in the coming year. Opportunities for involvement will increase their motivation, ownership, and interest in learning.

Use the One-Year Planning Grid to give yourself a broad overview of the year ahead. Start by shading in all other commitments that will impinge upon your school time—such as holidays, church commitments, travel, appointments, or big changes in your family (like moving or a new baby).

Once you have an accurate picture of just how much "real" time you have for your school year, it's time to commit the rest of your planning to prayer.

There are always trade-offs and hard choices to be made in homeschooling. You will not get everything done that is worthwhile—that's why you need to ask God to show you the limits of His work for you. You can't do it all. But by His grace, you can finish, and finish well, the work He's called you to.

Before adding further details to the overview of the school year, you need to figure out what goals God has for your family and for each child. Use the Student Goal Setter and the Family Priorities form for this.

Prayerfully list the goals He places on your heart. Trust that He'll supply the means in His perfect time. It's unlikely you will see these goals fully met during the year ahead, but this list will help you better focus your efforts and training. And above all, it will help you allocate time so your children will have the opportunity to develop greater strength in these areas.

Prioritize for Sanity

Goal setting is not enough. You will have to prioritize all the goals you list because your children's needs and objectives are constantly going to be in conflict with each other throughout your school day. This is a big reason why we as moms end up spending all our time putting out fires. We don't deal with the underlying causes of those interruptions. And we don't give each child a time he or she can count on our availability. The most demanding child or issue typically takes precedence. Prioritizing will help you faithfully distribute your time according to God's intentions in the midst of multiple goals.

Once you have determined the character and academic goals for each child, then determine whether or not a certain child's goals need to take priority over the others. For example, if you are potty-training, that's a task that can't be delayed by the needs of others.

Often we allocate our time to the oldest by default when it is actually our youngest children who need the most emotional and academic support from us. One year I determined that this would be my youngest child's year—her needs would come first. Of course, that wasn't fully possible, but that year she made the greatest gains because she finally had the time investment from me she needed.

Once you've decided your overall priorities for your children, use the Family Priorities form to sketch out how these goals should be nested under the larger goals you and your husband have for your family.

Homeschooling is just one part of the big picture of your family life. There are additional areas God calls us to be faithful in, and we need to plan so that homeschooling does not overshadow other obligations we have before God. Obviously, all the planning you do on your retreat should be done in pencil, and you should find time to talk through all of this with your husband before finalizing the coming year's plan.

Finally, resist the temptation to be overly ambitious. That's the point of prioritizing these goals. You are unlikely to have many school years where all your goals are realized. By prioritizing them, you can focus your greatest effort on your most important goals.

The remaining steps are designed to help you execute and maintain the plan you and your husband set.

Implement Monthly Planning Sessions (2 hours)

Tools:

- Monthly Planners (start with pages 26-27)
- Family Priorities form (page 22)

Purpose:

- Block time for family priorities.
- Set margins for your life.
- Tweak your plan.

In advance of each month, spend up to two hours blocking out time slots on the monthly planners according to your priorities and commitments. At the beginning of the school year, you will probably devote more time to planning, but as the year proceeds, your planning time will be reduced as you establish your routines. Routines grease the rails of harmonious family life—they reduce conflicts and increase efficiencies. (At one point in our household, we had a procedure for getting in and out of the van—just to stop the arguing over who sat where each time we left the house!)

During your monthly planning sessions, evaluate what tasks are consuming the bulk of your time. Does this time investment reflect your priorities? If not, can you bring greater order to these areas to reduce the time commitment? Since part of independent learning is realizing that others depend on you, can parts of these tasks be delegated to one of your older children?

Follow these steps in filling out the monthly planner pages:

- Review the prior month's plan and recall God's specific demonstrations of faithfulness and grace. Cultivate thankfulness for His activity.
- Use the Family Priorities form as your prayer list—ask God to supply the growth in these areas over the next month.
- Next, block out time on the new month for your priorities.
- Schedule down time. God designed us to need rest.
- Troubleshoot scheduling gridlock.
- Prayerfully consider whether all your commitments are from God.
- Thank God for the abundant grace He will give you to faithfully complete these commitments.

Rejuvenate with Weekly Planning Breaks (30 minutes)

Tools:

- Four-page Weekly Planners (start with pages 50–53)

Purpose:

- Recount God's faithfulness.
- Make a battle plan for the week ahead.
- Commit your plan to the Lord.

Here is where the story of God's activity in your homeschooling journey is set down for your future encouragement and the next generation. Schedule your weekly planning session at a time when the Lord's Day is still fresh in your mind. Use the first page of each week's planner to recount God's activity in your life, remind yourself of the truths of His Word, and sketch out a battle plan for facing the challenges of the week ahead. To combat temptation, arm yourself with at least one fighter verse (a particularly helpful reminder of God's faithfulness and power during times of challenge—see list at DesiringGod.org). Once freshly rejuvenated by His grace and faithfulness, then turn the page and let the planning begin!

The weekly planning grid is designed for maximum flexibility. You have six blocks across the top and six blocks down the left-hand side. How you organize these will depend upon the number of children you are schooling and the type of curriculum you use. Your main decision is whether to group each child's tasks by subject areas or day of the week. (See examples on pages 14-15. These visual representations will really help!) Play around with a few drafts to see what works best for you. Don't forget to include a plan for your younger children, as well as a column or row designating how your time will be distributed among your kids. If you live in a state that requires documentation, you can date or number the school days logged.

Depending upon whether you organize by subject area or day of the week, you will fill each block with what each child should complete in each subject that day or with a week's worth of work in each subject area. Check off work as it is completed.

Provide Monday Morning Tutorials (20 minutes per child)

Tools:

- This Week's Plan (as recorded on the Weekly Planner pages)
- *The Ultimate Daily Planner for Students* by Debra Bell
- *The Ultimate Weekly Planner for Teens* by Debra Bell

Purpose:

- Help each child develop time management skills.
- Clarify the week's assignments.
- Offer encouragement.
- Pray together.

The goal of these weekly meetings is to incrementally and strategically shift responsibility for planning the week's work from your shoulders to your child's. Ideally, this will happen by ninth grade, at which point you use the weekly tutorial to pre-approve the plan your teen has laid out. But that shift doesn't happen overnight. You incrementally move your children towards greater ownership and greater responsibility in managing their time.

Your planner and the teen planner organize time at a weekly level; the student planner organizes time at a daily level. Move your children to the teen planner only after they can responsibly and consistently manage their time well each day.

During the weekly tutorial, oversee each child's transferring of the week's work from your planner to his or her daily schedule of activities. During your planning time with teens, jointly agree on the work that should be assigned and accomplished. This is a time to provide support and encouragement as you clarify and negotiate the best way to organize the week's tasks. Don't overlook training them to seek God's help and grace in their own lives—especially where work is particularly challenging. Finish the tutorial by praying with your child.

Finish with Friday Afternoon Reviews (15 minutes per child)

Tools:

- This Week's Plan (as recorded on the Weekly Planner pages)
- *The Ultimate Daily Planner for Students*
- *The Ultimate Weekly Planner for Teens*

Purpose:

- Provide accountability.
- Offer feedback.

At least once a week, or more frequently if necessary, you need to provide accountability for all your kids—even your teens. A quick weekly review, with everyone's planner in hand, should keep you on top of how well your kids are managing their time, succeeding with tasks, or struggling to reach their academic or character goals. This information will help you use next week's planning session effectively.

Steps to Independence

1. Show student how to complete a task.
2. Complete the task with the student.
3. Watch student complete the task.
4. Student completes the task alone.
5. Student decides when the task needs to be done.

Use the table below to create a coding system for your planning. You may wish to create abbreviations for each child, subject, and repeated activities and events. Record this key in the front of each student's planner as well.

Key	Children/Subjects/Activities
S.A.	Sally Anne
R	reading
FT	field trip

Yearly Planning Retreat

First fill in the One-Year Planning Grid with events that will override your weekly schedule. Include days your husband may be off work, holidays, and extended family commitments.

Then add pre-scheduled commitments for your home-school, such as weekly co-op dates.

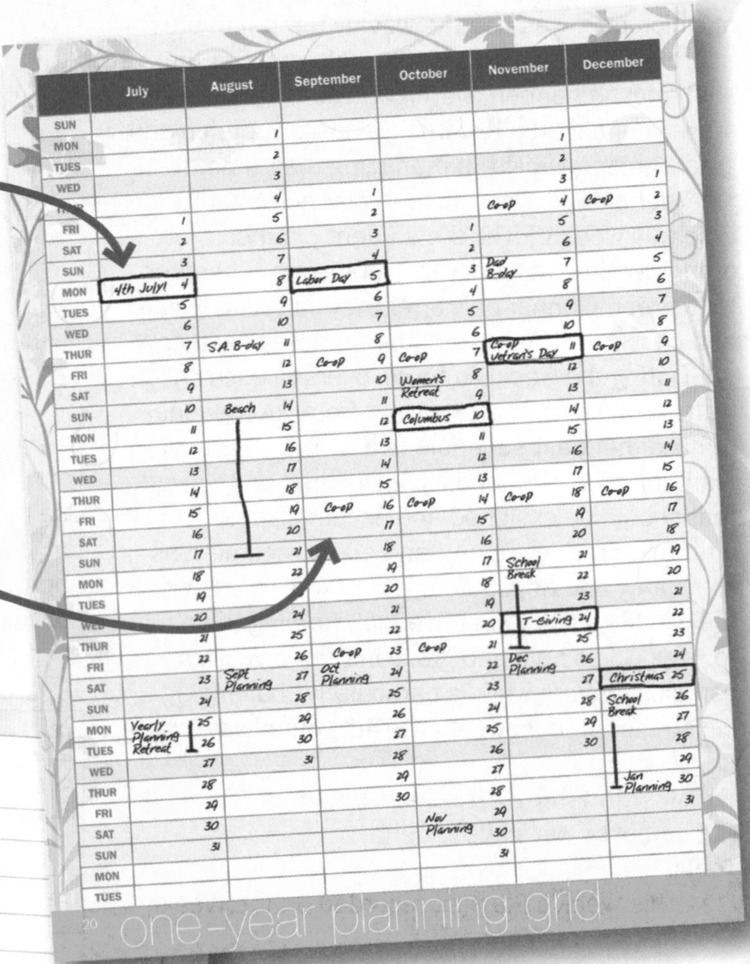

	July	August	September	October	November	December
SUN						
MON		1				
TUES		2			1	
WED		3			2	
THUR		4	1		3	1
FRI	1	5	2		Co-op 4	Co-op 2
SAT	2	6	3	1	5	3
SUN	3	7	4	2	6	4
MON	4th July! 4	8	Labor Day 5	3	Dad B-day 7	5
TUES	5	9	6	4	8	6
WED	6	10	7	5	9	7
THUR	7	S.A. B-day 11	8	6	10	8
FRI	8	12	Co-op 9	Co-op 7	Co-op Vetran's Day 11	Co-op 9
SAT	9	13	10	Women's Retreat 8	12	10
SUN	10	Beach 14	11	9	13	11
MON	11	15	12	Columbus 10	14	12
TUES	12	16	13	11	15	13
WED	13	17	14	12	16	14
THUR	14	18	15	13	17	15
FRI	15	19	Co-op 16	Co-op 14	Co-op 18	Co-op 16
SAT	16	20	17	15	19	17
SUN	17	21	18	16	20	18
MON	18	22	19	17	School Break 21	19
TUES	19	23	20	18	22	20
WED	20	24	21	19	23	21
THUR	21	25	22	20	T-Giving 24	22
FRI	22	26	Co-op 23	Co-op 21	25	23
SAT	23	Sept Planning 27	Oct Planning 24	22	Dec Planning 26	24
SUN	24	28	25	23	27	Christmas 25
MON	Yearly Planning Retreat 25	29	26	24	28	School Break 26
TUES	26	30	27	25	29	27
WED	27	31	28	26	30	28
THUR	28		29	27		29
FRI	29		30	28		Jan Planning 30
SAT	30			Nov Planning 29		31
SUN	31			30		
MON				31		
TUES						

20 one-year planning grid

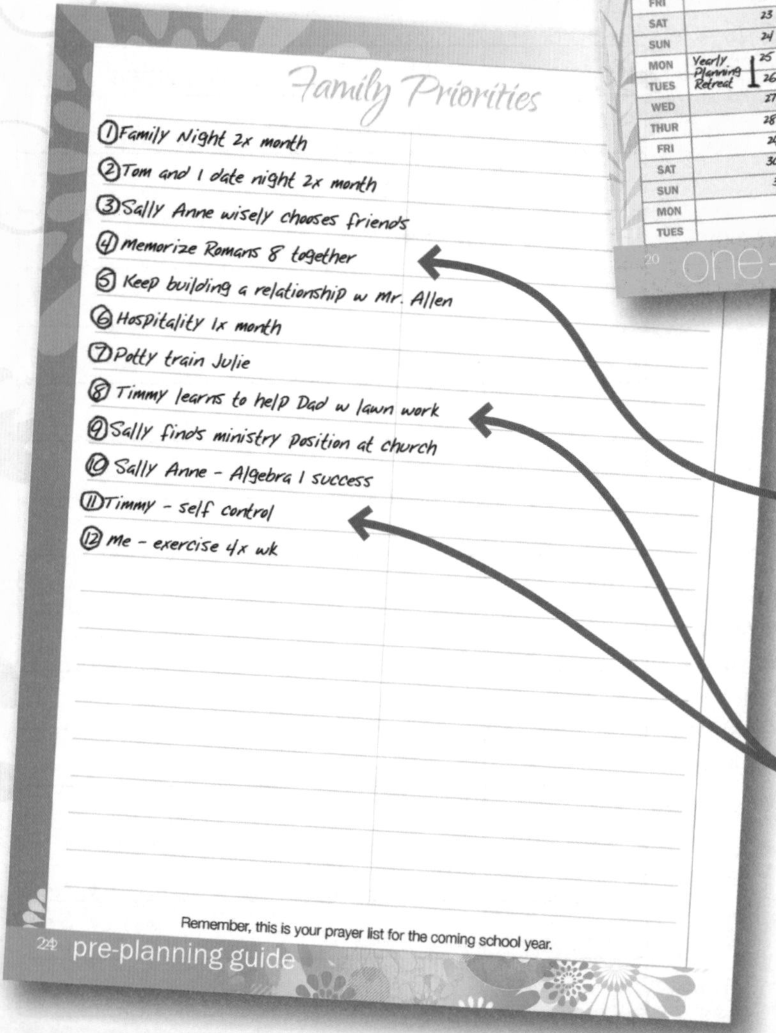

Family Priorities

1. Family Night 2x month
2. Tom and I date night 2x month
3. Sally Anne wisely chooses friends
4. Memorize Romans 8 together
5. Keep building a relationship w Mr. Allen
6. Hospitality 1x month
7. Potty train Julie
8. Timmy learns to help Dad w lawn work
9. Sally finds ministry position at church
10. Sally Anne - Algebra I success
11. Timmy - self control
12. me - exercise 4x wk

Remember, this is your prayer list for the coming school year.

24 pre-planning guide

In conjunction with your husband, determine the goals you want to focus on for the coming school year. Then prioritize them on the Family Priorities form.

Determine which student goals will take precedence.

Review the previous year with each school-age child before your yearly planning retreat. Older kids should participate in setting their academic and character goals for the coming year.

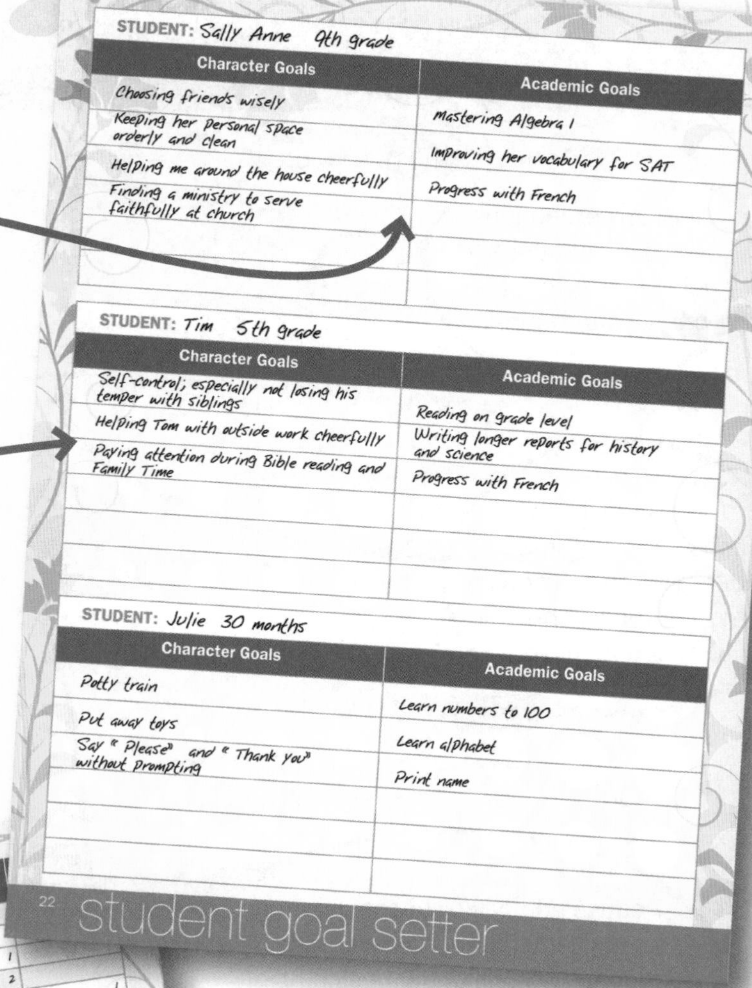

STUDENT: Sally Anne 9th grade

Character Goals	Academic Goals
Choosing friends wisely	Mastering Algebra I
Keeping her personal space orderly and clean	Improving her vocabulary for SAT
Helping me around the house cheerfully	Progress with French
Finding a ministry to serve faithfully at church	

STUDENT: Tim 5th grade

Character Goals	Academic Goals
Self-control; especially not losing his temper with siblings	Reading on grade level
Helping Tom with outside work cheerfully	Writing longer reports for history and science
Paying attention during Bible reading and Family Time	Progress with French

STUDENT: Julie 30 months

Character Goals	Academic Goals
Potty train	Learn numbers to 100
Put away toys	Learn alphabet
Say "Please" and "Thank you" without prompting	Print name

22 student goal setter

Use the Student Goal Setter forms to set character and academic goals for each of your children.

July
August
September
October
November
4th July!
Begin Potty Training
S.A. B-day
Beach
Labor Day
Co-op
Sept Planning
Yearly Planning Retreat
Women's Retreat
Columbus
Oct Planning
Dad B-day
Co-op Veteran's Day
School Break
T-Giving
Dec Planning
Plan Surprise Party
Mr. Allen B-day Party
Nov Planning
Christmas
School Break
Jan Planning
Memorize Romans 8
20 one-year planning grid

Now figure out the best time to tackle the long-term goals on your Family Priorities form, such as potty training a toddler. The goal is to avoid scheduling gridlock.

Monthly Planning Sessions

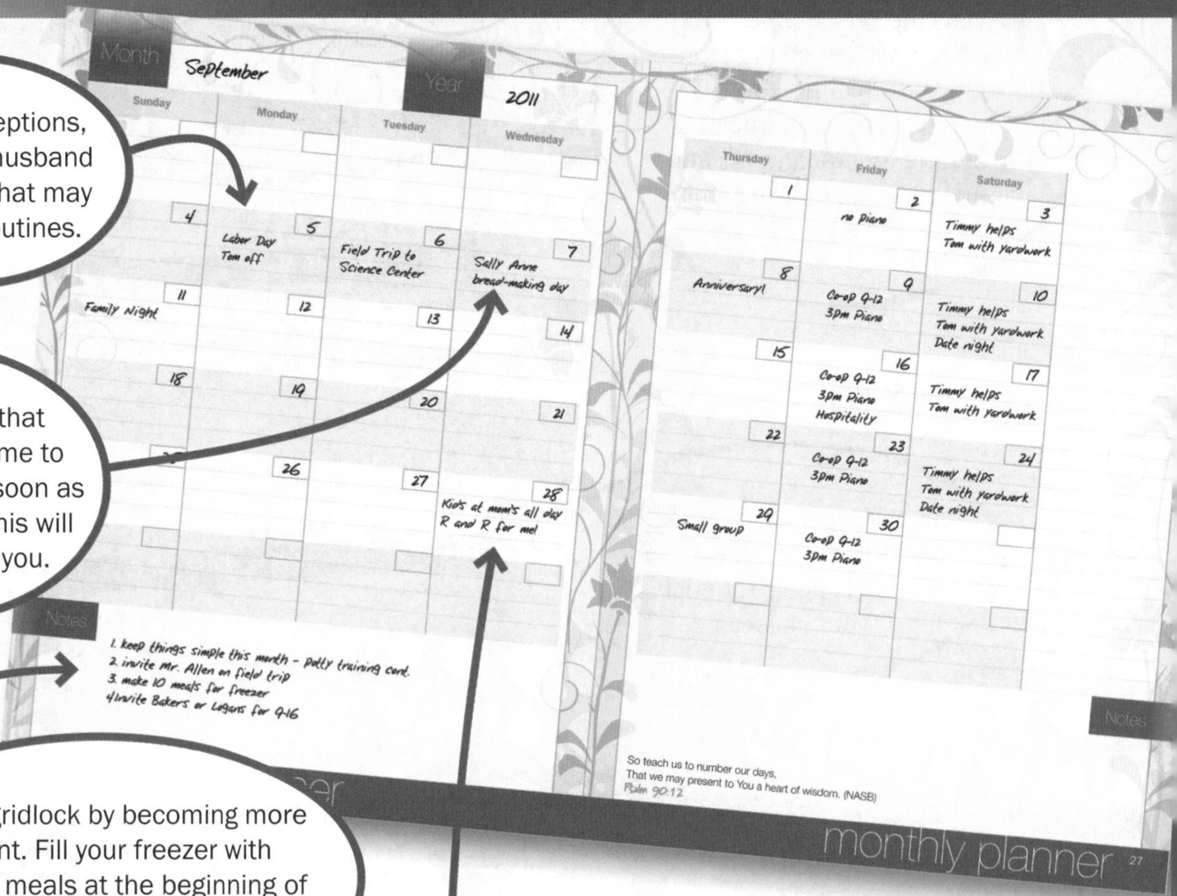
Month
September
Year
2011
Sunday
Monday
Tuesday
Wednesday
Thursday
Friday
Saturday
1
2
no Piano
3
Timmy helps Tom with Yardwork
4
5
Labor Day Tom off
6
Field Trip to Science Center
7
Sally Anne bread-making day
8
Anniversary!
9
Co-op 9-12 3pm Piano
10
Timmy helps Tom with Yardwork Date night
11
Family Night
12
13
14
15
16
Co-op 9-12 3pm Piano Hospitality
17
Timmy helps Tom with Yardwork
18
19
20
21
22
23
Co-op 9-12 3pm Piano
24
Timmy helps Tom with Yardwork Date night
26
27
28
Kids at mom's all day R and R for me!
29
Small group
30
Co-op 9-12 3pm Piano
Notes
1. keep things simple this month - potty training cont.
2. invite Mr. Allen on field trip
3. make 10 meals for freezer
4. invite Bakers or Logans for 9-16
Notes
So teach us to number our days,
That we may present to You a heart of wisdom. (NASB)
Psalm 90:12
monthly planner 27

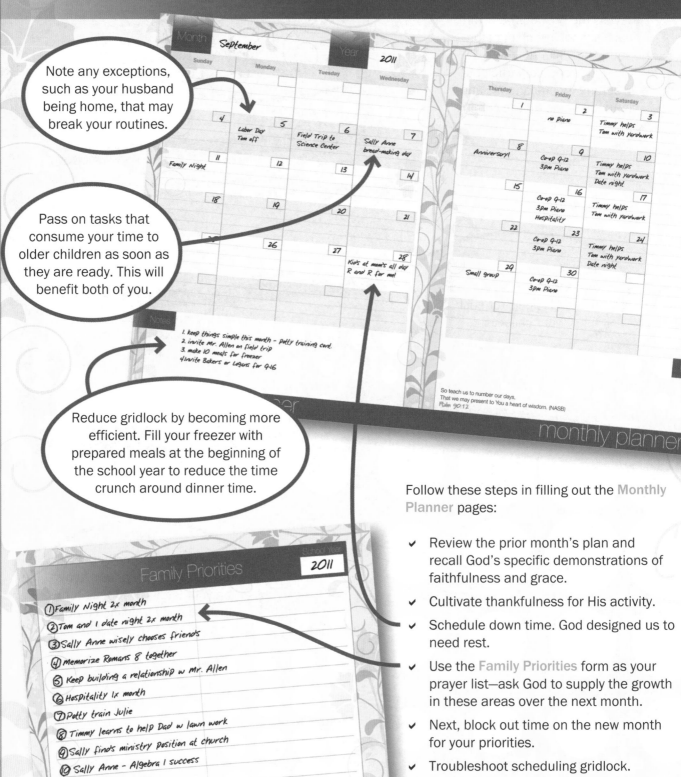

Note any exceptions, such as your husband being home, that may break your routines.

Pass on tasks that consume your time to older children as soon as they are ready. This will benefit both of you.

Reduce gridlock by becoming more efficient. Fill your freezer with prepared meals at the beginning of the school year to reduce the time crunch around dinner time.

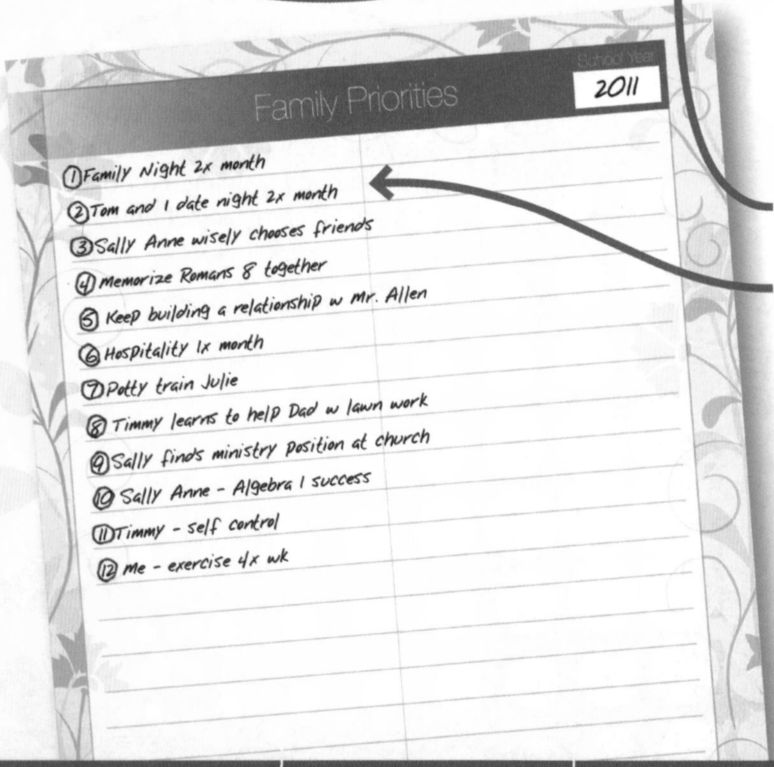
Family Priorities
School Year
2011
① Family Night 2x month
② Tom and I date night 2x month
③ Sally Anne wisely chooses friends
④ memorize Romans 8 together
⑤ Keep building a relationship w Mr. Allen
⑥ Hospitality 1x month
⑦ Potty train Julie
⑧ Timmy learns to help Dad w lawn work
⑨ Sally finds ministry position at church
⑩ Sally Anne - Algebra I success
⑪ Timmy - self control
⑫ me - exercise 4x wk

Follow these steps in filling out the **Monthly Planner** pages:

- Review the prior month's plan and recall God's specific demonstrations of faithfulness and grace.
- Cultivate thankfulness for His activity.
- Schedule down time. God designed us to need rest.
- Use the **Family Priorities** form as your prayer list—ask God to supply the growth in these areas over the next month.
- Next, block out time on the new month for your priorities.
- Troubleshoot scheduling gridlock.
- Prayerfully consider if all your commitments are from God.
- Thank God for the abundant grace He will give you to faithfully complete these commitments.

Weekly Planning Breaks

Follow these steps in filling out the Weekly Planner pages:

- Begin each week with a planning session in a quiet place.
- Start by recounting God's faithfulness during the prior week.
- Commit to make God's Word a central part of your plan for peace.
- Consider the areas where you are most vulnerable. Prayerfully outline a battle plan to overcome temptation.
- A list of fighter verses is available free of charge at DesiringGod.org.

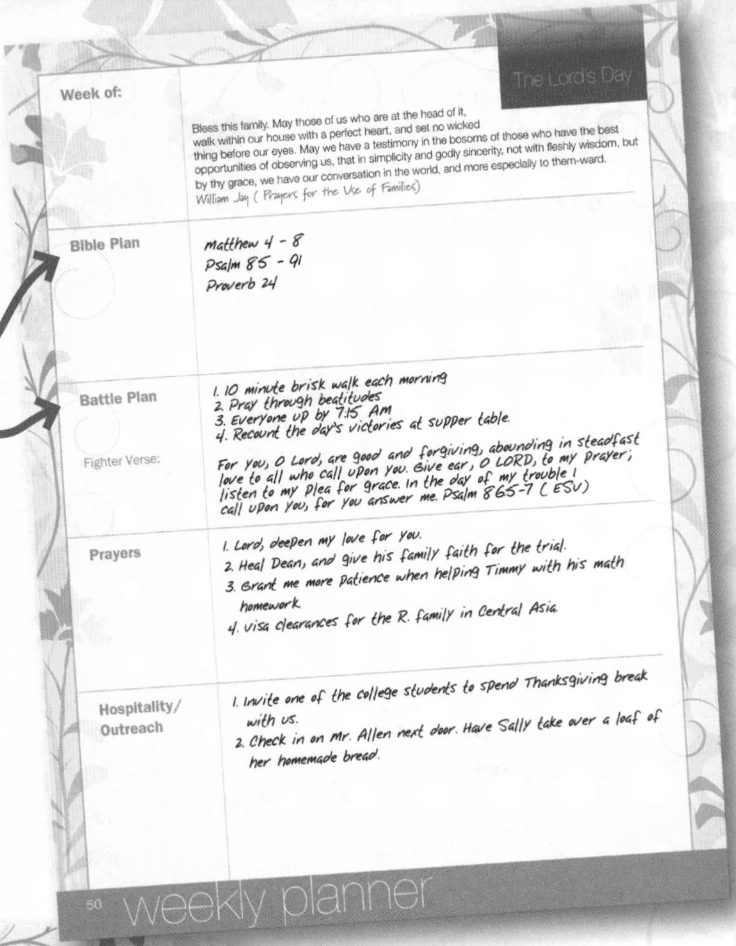

The Lord's Day

Week of:	Bless this family. May those of us who are at the head of it, walk within our house with a perfect heart, and set no wicked thing before our eyes. May we have a testimony in the bosoms of those who have the best opportunities of observing us, that in simplicity and godly sincerity, not with fleshly wisdom, but by thy grace, we have our conversation in the world, and more especially to them-ward. William Jay (Prayers for the Use of Families)
Bible Plan	Matthew 4 - 8 Psalm 85 - 91 Proverb 24
Battle Plan	1. 10 minute brisk walk each morning 2. Pray through beatitudes 3. Everyone up by 7:15 AM 4. Recount the day's victories at supper table.
Fighter Verse:	For you, O Lord, are good and forgiving, abounding in steadfast love to all who call upon you. Give ear, O LORD, to my prayer; listen to my plea for grace. In the day of my trouble I call upon you, for you answer me. Psalm 86:5-7 (ESV)
Prayers	1. Lord, deepen my love for you. 2. Heal Dean, and give his family faith for the trial. 3. Grant me more patience when helping Timmy with his math homework. 4. visa clearances for the R. family in Central Asia.
Hospitality/ Outreach	1. Invite one of the college students to spend Thanksgiving break with us. 2. Check in on Mr. Allen next door. Have Sally take over a loaf of her homemade bread.

50 weekly planner

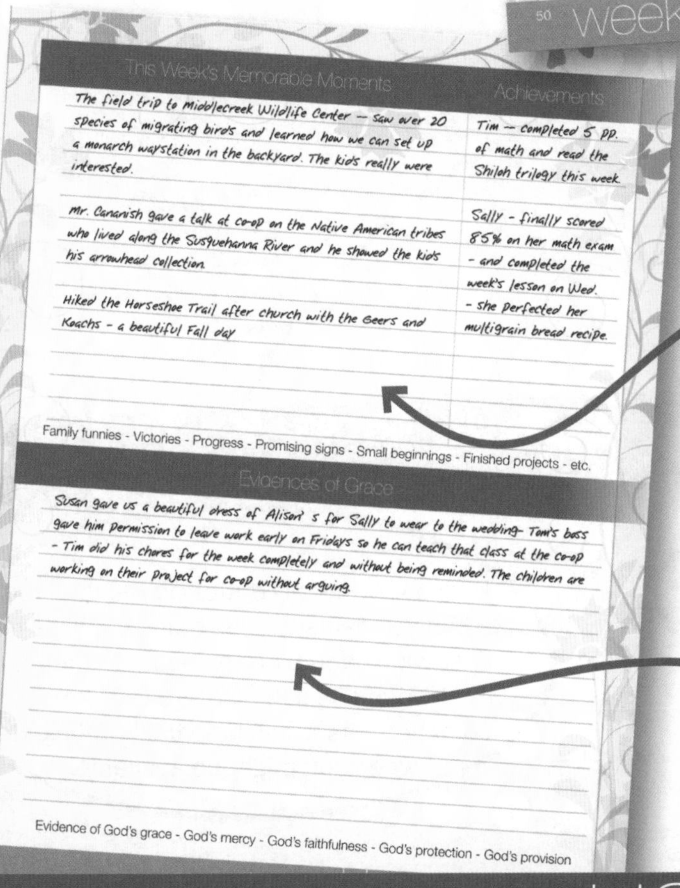

This Week's Memorable Moments	Achievements
The field trip to Middlecreek Wildlife Center -- saw over 20 species of migrating birds and learned how we can set up a monarch waystation in the backyard. The kids really were interested.	Tim -- completed 5 pp. of math and read the Shiloh trilogy this week.
Mr. Canarish gave a talk at co-op on the Native American tribes who lived along the Susquehanna River and he showed the kids his arrowhead collection.	Sally - finally scored 85% on her math exam - and completed the week's lesson on Wed.
Hiked the Horseshoe Trail after church with the Geers and Koachs - a beautiful Fall day	- she perfected her multigrain bread recipe.

Family funnies - Victories - Progress - Promising signs - Small beginnings - Finished projects - etc.

Evidences of Grace

Susan gave us a beautiful dress of Alison's for Sally to wear to the wedding - Tom's boss gave him permission to leave work early on Fridays so he can teach that class at the co-op - Tim did his chores for the week completely and without being reminded. The children are working on their project for co-op without arguing.

Evidence of God's grace - God's mercy - God's faithfulness - God's protection - God's provision

Write down all signs of forward momentum. (Your kids are going to peek in here to see what you find noteworthy.) Show them how to celebrate small beginnings and promising signs.

Taking time to document God's particular kindnesses and evidences of grace in your family's life will build your faith for the future and create a family heirloom for future generations.

Weekly Planning Breaks

The Weekly Planner grid is designed for maximum flexibility. You can organize the rows across the top and columns down the left-hand side by day of the week, subject area, or children. If you live in a state that requires documentation, then you can track the number of school days in the blocks as well.

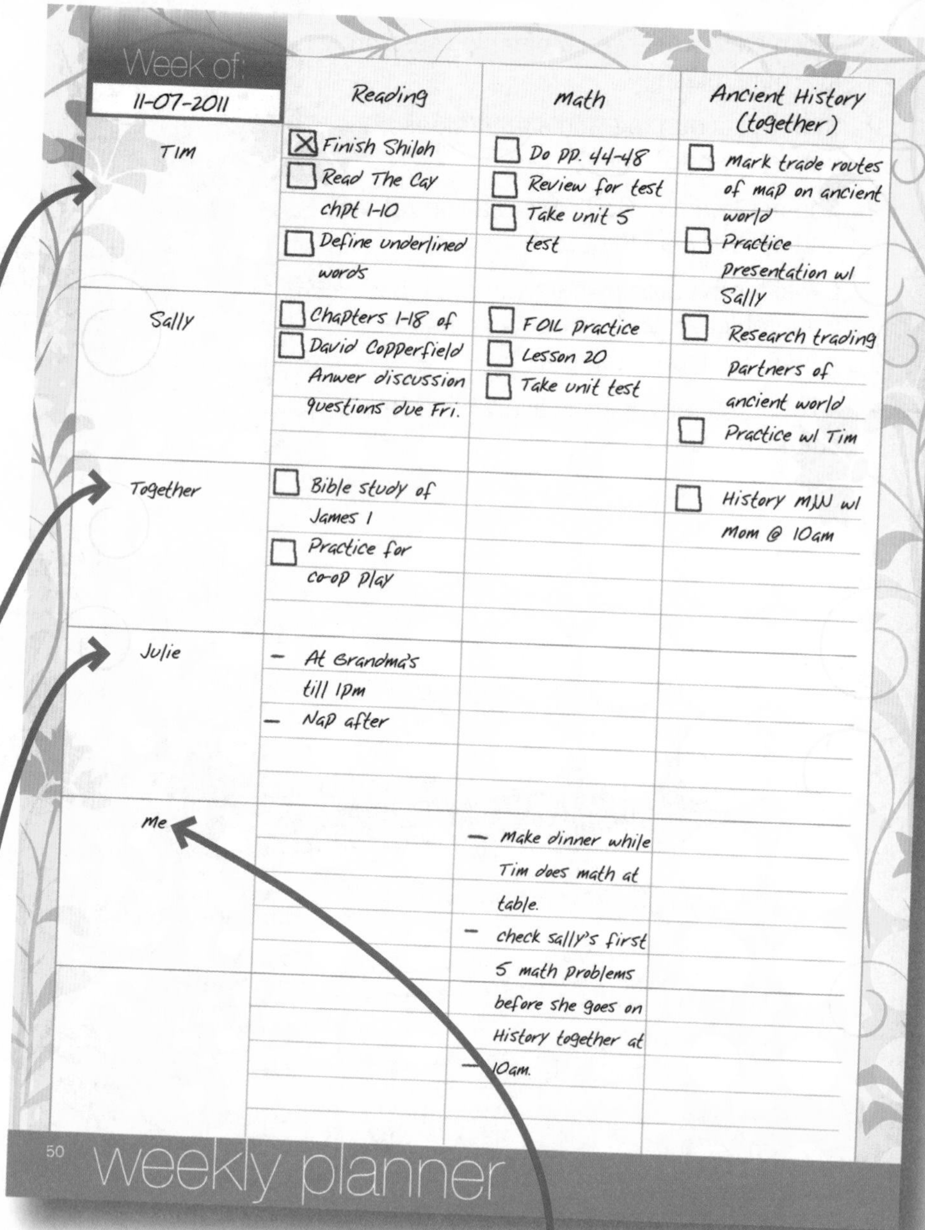

Week of: 11-07-2011	Reading	Math	Ancient History (together)
TIM	☒ Finish Shiloh ☐ Read The Cay chpt 1-10 ☐ Define underlined words	☐ Do pp. 44-48 ☐ Review for test ☐ Take unit 5 test	☐ Mark trade routes of map on ancient world ☐ Practice presentation w/ Sally
Sally	☐ Chapters 1-18 of ☐ David Copperfield Anwer discussion questions due Fri.	☐ FOIL practice ☐ Lesson 20 ☐ Take unit test	☐ Research trading partners of ancient world ☐ Practice w/ Tim
Together	☐ Bible study of James 1 ☐ Practice for co-op play		☐ History M/W w/ Mom @ 10am
Julie	– At Grandma's till 1pm – Nap after		
Me		– Make dinner while Tim does math at table. – check Sally's first 5 math problems before she goes on History together at – 10am.	

50 weekly planner

In this example, the blocks show what an individual child must complete in one subject area that week.

If you use a unit study curriculum designed for multiple grade levels, then designate one column or row for work completed as a family.

Plan for little ones as well. Think through what they will do while you are helping an older child.

Put your own daily duties on the grid, too. Then you can see scheduling conflicts in advance and plan to negotiate them. If your kids can also see your time commitments, it will help them anticipate when you might be available.

In this example, the grid is organized by days of the week, and the blocks contain what each student must complete that day. This is a good approach if you are not teaching any subjects together or if students need daily accountability for their work.

Week of: 11-07-2011	Tim	Sally	Me
Monday	☐ Bible James 1 ☐ Tutorial @ 8 am ☐ Reading-Finish Shiloh ☐ Math Lesson 19 ☐ French - Teach me Lesson 1	☐ Bible James 1 ☐ Tutorial 8:30 am ☐ Reading-David Copperfield ☐ Math-FOIL review ☐ French- Lesson 5	☐ Bible James 1 ☐ Work with Tim math lesson ☐ Look over Sally's FOIL review ☐ Get ready for history test
Tuesday	☐ Bible James 1 ☐ Reading - start The Cay ☐ Math - Check lesson 19 ☐ History trade route	☐ Bible James 1 ☐ Reading D.C. ☐ Math-Start lesson 20 ☐ Start of research of trading partners	☐ Bible James 1 ☐ Teach history lesson in afternoon
Wednesday	☐ Bible James 1 ☐ Science Lesson AM with Mr Allen ☐ History discussion pm ☐ math review for unit test Fri	☐ Bible James 1 ☐ Science Lesson AM with Mr Allen ☐ History discussion pm ☐ math review for test	☐ Bible James 1 ☐ Science Lesson AM ☐ History discussion questions during naptime ☐ midweek math check
Thursday			

Ask students to check off work as it is completed. Then you have a quick way to check their progress.

weekly planner

Key	Children/Subjects/Activities
S.A.	Sally Anne
R	reading
FT	field trip

Maximize the space in each block by creating a coding system for common entries—e.g., names of subjects, children, texts, activities.

Monday Morning Tutorials

Meet with each student for approximately 20 minutes. During this time, you should do the following:

- ✔ Help each child develop time management skills.
- ✔ Clarify the week's assignments.
- ✔ Encourage your child to recognize God's grace and activity in completing these tasks.
- ✔ Pray together and build faith for the week ahead.

Students using *The Ultimate Daily Planner for Students* should copy their assignments from your planner to their planner during this time.

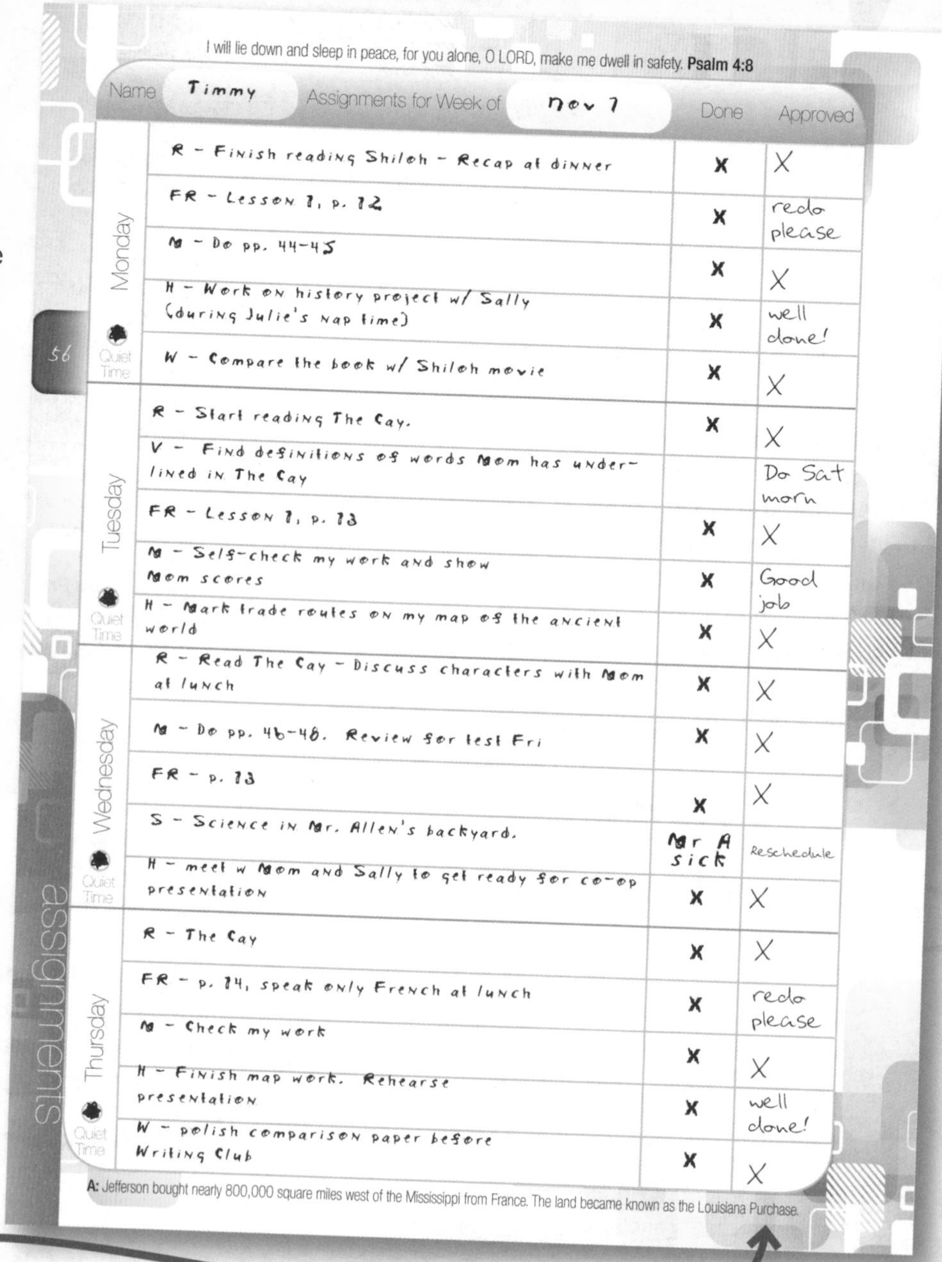

I will lie down and sleep in peace, for you alone, O LORD, make me dwell in safety. **Psalm 4:8**

Name: Timmy — Assignments for Week of: Nov 7

Day	Assignment	Done	Approved
Monday	R - Finish reading Shiloh - Recap at dinner	X	X
	FR - Lesson 7, p. 12	X	redo please
	M - Do pp. 44-45	X	X
	H - Work on history project w/ Sally (during Julie's nap time)	X	well done!
	W - Compare the book w/ Shiloh movie	X	X
Tuesday	R - Start reading The Cay.	X	X
	V - Find definitions of words Mom has underlined in The Cay		Do Sat morn
	FR - Lesson 7, p. 13	X	X
	M - Self-check my work and show Mom scores	X	Good job
	H - Mark trade routes on my map of the ancient world	X	X
Wednesday	R - Read The Cay - Discuss characters with Mom at lunch	X	X
	M - Do pp. 46-48. Review for test Fri	X	X
	FR - p. 13	X	X
	S - Science in Mr. Allen's backyard.	Mr A sick	Reschedule
	H - meet w Mom and Sally to get ready for co-op presentation	X	X
Thursday	R - The Cay	X	X
	FR - p. 14, speak only French at lunch	X	redo please
	M - Check my work	X	X
	H - Finish map work. Rehearse presentation	X	well done!
	W - polish comparison paper before Writing Club	X	X

A: Jefferson bought nearly 800,000 square miles west of the Mississippi from France. The land became known as the Louisiana Purchase.

Friday Afternoon Reviews

A quick weekly review, with everyone's planner in hand, should keep you on top of how well your kids are managing their time, succeeding with tasks, or struggling to reach their academic or character goals. Use this time to help you do the following:

- ✔ Provide accountability.
- ✔ Offer feedback and encouragement.
- ✔ Note areas that need your attention.

Example page from *The Ultimate Daily Planner for Students*

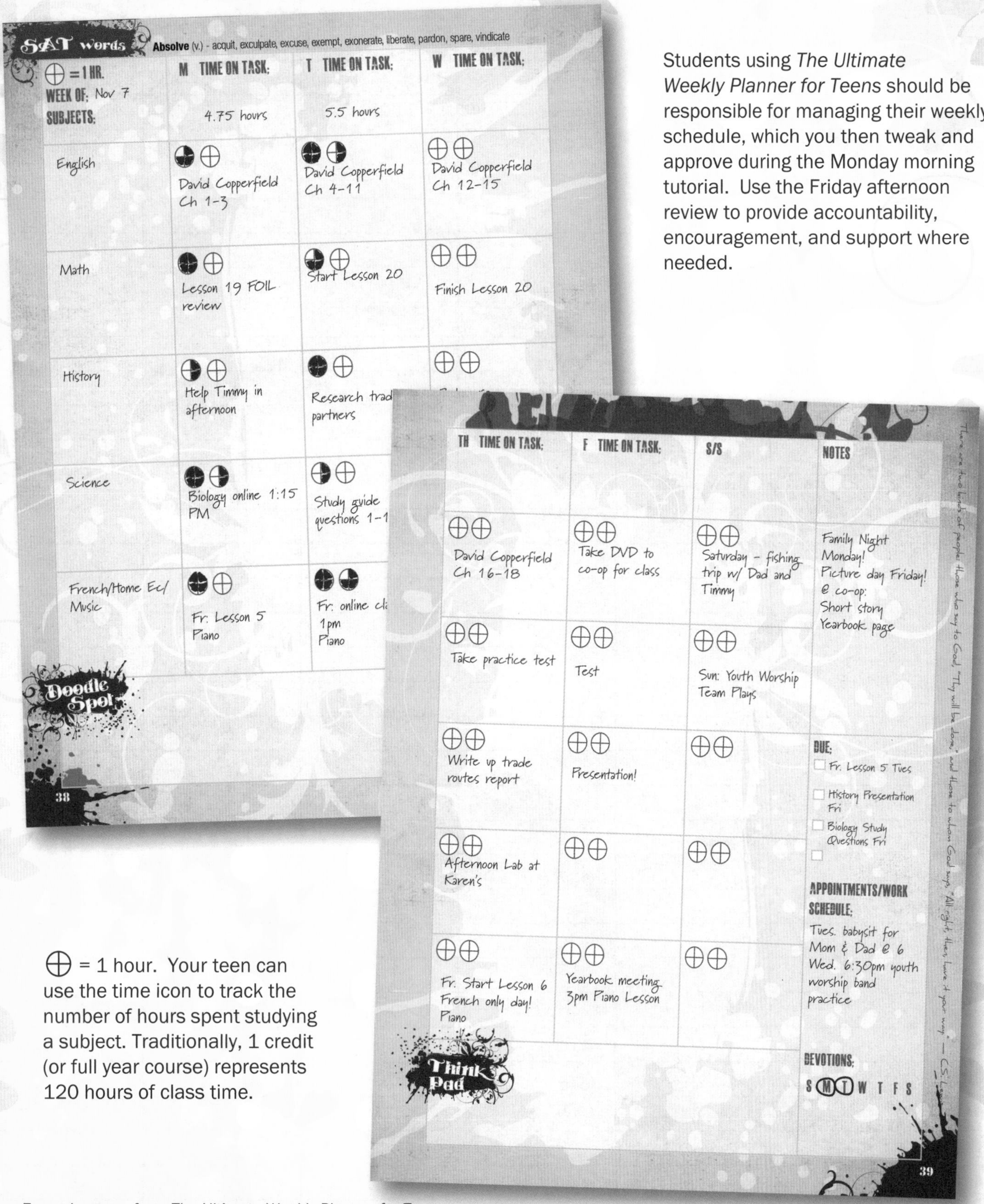

Students using *The Ultimate Weekly Planner for Teens* should be responsible for managing their weekly schedule, which you then tweak and approve during the Monday morning tutorial. Use the Friday afternoon review to provide accountability, encouragement, and support where needed.

⊕ = 1 hour. Your teen can use the time icon to track the number of hours spent studying a subject. Traditionally, 1 credit (or full year course) represents 120 hours of class time.

Example pages from *The Ultimate Weekly Planner for Teens*

	July	August	September	October	November	December
SUN						
MON						
TUES						
WED						
THUR						
FRI						
SAT						
SUN						
MON						
TUES						
WED						
THUR						
FRI						
SAT						
SUN						
MON						
TUES						
WED						
THUR						
FRI						
SAT						
SUN						
MON						
TUES						
WED						
THUR						
FRI						
SAT						
SUN						
MON						
TUES						
WED						
THUR						
FRI						
SAT						
SUN						
MON						
TUES						

January	February	March	April	May	June	
						SUN
						MON
						TUES
						WED
						THUR
						FRI
						SAT
						SUN
						MON
						TUES
						WED
						THUR
						FRI
						SAT
						SUN
						MON
						TUES
						WED
						THUR
						FRI
						SAT
						SUN
						MON
						TUES
						WED
						THUR
						FRI
						SAT
						SUN
						MON
						TUES
						WED
						THUR
						FRI
						SAT
						SUN
						MON
						TUES

STUDENT:

Character Goals	Academic Goals

STUDENT:

Character Goals	Academic Goals

STUDENT:

Character Goals	Academic Goals

STUDENT:

Character Goals	Academic Goals

STUDENT:

Character Goals	Academic Goals

STUDENT:

Character Goals	Academic Goals

Family Priorities

School Year

Remember, this is your prayer list for the coming school year.

Student	Student
Resource List	Resource List

Use this form to list the resources you are planning to use with each child.

Student	Student
Resource List	**Resource List**

Use this form to list the resources you are planning to use with each child.

Student	Student
Resource List	Resource List

Use this form to list the resources you are planning to use with each child.

Month

Year

Sunday	Monday	Tuesday	Wednesday

Notes

Thursday	Friday	Saturday

It is God to whom and with whom we travel, and while He is the end of our journey, He is also at every stopping place.
Elisabeth Elliot

Notes

He has made everything beautiful in its time. He has also set eternity in the hearts of men; yet they cannot fathom what God has done from beginning to end.
Ecclesiastes 3:11

Month Year

Sunday	Monday	Tuesday	Wednesday

Notes

Who dares to teach must never cease to learn.
John Cotton Dana

Thursday	Friday	Saturday

Notes

So teach us to number our days,
That we may present to You a heart of wisdom.
Psalm 90:12, NASB

Month Year

Sunday	Monday	Tuesday	Wednesday

Notes

One sees great things from the valley; only small things from the peak.
G. K. Chesterton

Thursday	Friday	Saturday

Notes

"For I know the plans I have for you," declares the LORD, "plans to prosper you and not to harm you, plans to give you hope and a future."
Jeremiah 29:11

Month Year

Sunday	Monday	Tuesday	Wednesday

Notes

Thursday	Friday	Saturday

Imagination is more important than knowledge. Knowledge is limited. Imagination encircles the world.
Albert Einstein

Notes

Commit to the LORD whatever you do, and your plans will succeed.
Proverbs 16:3

Month Year

Sunday	Monday	Tuesday	Wednesday

Notes

Thursday	Friday	Saturday

The children should have the joy of living in far lands, in other persons, in other times—a delightful double existence; and this joy they will find, for the most part, in their story books.
Charlotte Mason

Notes

The heart of man plans his way, but the Lord establishes his steps.
Proverbs 16:9, ESV

Month

Year

Sunday	Monday	Tuesday	Wednesday

Notes

Thursday	Friday	Saturday

Many things can wait. Children cannot. Today their bones are being formed, their blood is being made, their senses are being developed. To them we cannot say "tomorrow." Their name is today.

Gabriela Mistral

Notes

And do this, understanding the present time. The hour has come for you to wake up from your slumber, because our salvation is nearer now than when we first believed. The night is nearly over; the day is almost here. So let us put aside the deeds of darkness and put on the armor of light.

Romans 13:11-12

Month Year

Sunday	Monday	Tuesday	Wednesday

Notes

There is nothing worth living for, unless it is worth dying for.
attributed to Elisabeth Elliot

Thursday	Friday	Saturday

Notes

Walk in wisdom toward outsiders, making the best use of the time. Let your speech always be gracious, seasoned with salt, so that you may know how you ought to answer each person.
Colossians 4:5–6, ESV

Month Year

Sunday	Monday	Tuesday	Wednesday

Notes

I cannot teach anybody anything, I can only make them think.
Socrates

Thursday	Friday	Saturday

Notes

Show this same diligence to the very end, in order to make your hope sure. We do not want you to become lazy, but to imitate those who through faith and patience inherit what has been promised.
Hebrews 6:11-12

Month

Year

Sunday	Monday	Tuesday	Wednesday

Notes

Love is not blind; that is the last thing that it is. Love is bound; and the more it is bound the less it is blind.
G. K. Chesterton

Thursday	Friday	Saturday

Notes

Be careful then how you live, not as unwise people but as wise, making the most of the time, because the days are evil. So do not be foolish, but understand what the will of the Lord is.
Ephesians 5:15–17, NRSV

Month

Year

Sunday	Monday	Tuesday	Wednesday

Notes

Nine tenths of education is encouragement.
Anatole France

Thursday	Friday	Saturday

Notes

For he says, "In a favorable time I listened to you, and in a day of salvation I have helped you." Behold, now is the favorable time; behold, now is the day of salvation.
2 Corinthians 6:2, ESV

Month		Year	

Sunday	Monday	Tuesday	Wednesday

Notes

Thursday	Friday	Saturday

The question is not, how much does the youth know? when he has finished his education, but how much does he care?
Charlotte Mason

Notes

Whatever you do, work at it with all your heart, as working for the Lord, not for men, since you know that you will receive an inheritance from the Lord as a reward. It is the Lord Christ you are serving.
Colossians 3:23-24

Month

Year

Sunday	Monday	Tuesday	Wednesday

Notes

Thursday	Friday	Saturday

Getting things done is not always what is most important. There is value in allowing others to learn, even if the task is not accomplished as quickly, efficiently, or effectively.
R. D. Clyde

Notes

May the favor of the Lord our God rest on us; establish the work of our hands for us—yes, establish the work of our hands.
Psalm 90:17

The Lord's Day

Week of:

Bless this family. May those of us who are at the head of it walk within our house with a perfect heart, and set no wicked thing before our eyes. May we have a testimony in the bosoms of those who have the best opportunities of observing us, that in simplicity and godly sincerity, not with fleshly wisdom, but by thy grace, we have our conversation in the world, and more especially to them.
William Jay

Bible Plan

Battle Plan

Fighter Verse:

Prayers

Hospitality/ Outreach

This Week's Memorable Moments

Achievements

Family funnies - Victories - Progress - Promising signs - Small beginnings - Finished projects

Evidences of Grace

Evidence of God's grace - God's mercy - God's faithfulness - God's protection - God's provision

Week of:

Notes

Supplies

Appointments

Education is not the filling of a pail, but the lighting of a fire.
William Butler Yeats

Week of:	**The Lord's Day** Whence comes this idea that if what we are doing is fun, it can't be God's will? The God who made giraffes, a baby's fingernails, a puppy's tail, a crooknecked squash, the bobwhite's call, and a young girl's giggle, has a sense of humor. Make no mistake about that. *Catherine Marshall*
Bible Plan	
Battle Plan Fighter Verse:	
Prayers	
Hospitality/ Outreach	

This Week's Memorable Moments

Achievements

Family funnies - Victories - Progress - Promising signs - Small beginnings - Finished projects

Evidences of Grace

Evidence of God's grace - God's mercy - God's faithfulness - God's protection - God's provision

Week of:

Notes

Supplies

Appointments

The only time I ever find my dealings with God less than clear-cut is when I'm not being honest with Him. The fuzziness is always on my side, not His.
Catherine Marshall

Week of:	Fight for us, O God, that we not drift numb and blind and foolish into vain and empty excitements. Life is too short, too precious, too painful to waste on worldly bubbles that burst. Heaven is too great, hell is too horrible, eternity is too long that we should putter around on the porch of eternity. *John Piper*
Bible Plan	
Battle Plan Fighter Verse:	
Prayers	
Hospitality/ Outreach	

This Week's Memorable Moments

Achievements

Family funnies - Victories - Progress - Promising signs - Small beginnings - Finished projects

Evidences of Grace

Evidence of God's grace - God's mercy - God's faithfulness - God's protection - God's provision

Week of:

Notes

Supplies

Appointments

Patience to wait does not come from suffering long for what we lack but from sitting long in what we have.
Beth Moore

The Lord's Day

Week of:

Come, Lord Jesus, and abide in my heart. How grateful I am to realize that the answer to my prayer does not depend on me at all. As I quietly abide in You and let Your life flow into me, what freedom it is to know that the Father does not see my threadbare patience or insufficient trust, rather only Your patience, Lord, and Your confidence that the Father has everything in hand. In Your faith I thank You right now for a more glorious answer to my prayer than I can imagine. Amen.

Catherine Marshall

Bible Plan

Battle Plan

Fighter Verse:

Prayers

Hospitality/ Outreach

This Week's Memorable Moments

Achievements

Family funnies - Victories - Progress - Promising signs - Small beginnings - Finished projects

Evidences of Grace

Evidence of God's grace - God's mercy - God's faithfulness - God's protection - God's provision

Week of:

Notes

Supplies

Appointments

A kindhearted woman gains respect.
Proverbs 11:16

Week of:	The Lord's Day He that has trained his children for heaven, rather than for earth—for God rather than for man—he is the parent that will be called wise at the last. J. C. Ryle
Bible Plan	
Battle Plan Fighter Verse:	
Prayers	
Hospitality/ Outreach	

This Week's Memorable Moments

Achievements

Family funnies - Victories - Progress - Promising signs - Small beginnings - Finished projects

Evidences of Grace

Evidence of God's grace - God's mercy - God's faithfulness - God's protection - God's provision

Week of:

Notes

Supplies

Appointments

Anxiety does not empty tomorrow of its sorrows, but only empties today of its strength.
Charles Spurgeon

Week of:	Lord, High and Holy, Meek and Lowly . . . Let me learn by paradox that the way down is the way up, that to be low is to be high, that the broken heart is the healed heart, that the contrite spirit is the rejoicing spirit, that the repenting soul is the victorious soul, that to have nothing is to possess all, that to bear the cross is to wear the crown. *Puritan prayer*
Bible Plan	
Battle Plan Fighter Verse:	
Prayers	
Hospitality/ Outreach	

This Week's Memorable Moments | Achievements

Family funnies - Victories - Progress - Promising signs - Small beginnings - Finished projects

Evidences of Grace

Evidence of God's grace - God's mercy - God's faithfulness - God's protection - God's provision

Week of:

Notes

Supplies

Appointments

Wrinkles should merely indicate where smiles have been.
Mark Twain

Week of:	**The Lord's Day** Lord, we therefore bless thee for the return of a day sacred to our souls and eternity; a time of refreshing in the presence of the Lord: in which by waiting upon Thee our hearts are enlarged—and our strength is renewed—so that we can mount up as with wings of eagles, run and not be weary, walk and not faint. *William Jay*
Bible Plan	
Battle Plan Fighter Verse:	
Prayers	
Hospitality/ Outreach	

This Week's Memorable Moments

Achievements

Family funnies - Victories - Progress - Promising signs - Small beginnings - Finished projects

Evidences of Grace

Evidence of God's grace - God's mercy - God's faithfulness - God's protection - God's provision

Week of:

Notes

Supplies

Appointments

It's a good thing to have all the props pulled out from under us occasionally. It gives us some sense of what is rock under our feet, and what is sand.
Madeleine L'Engle

Week of:

Normal day, let me be aware of the treasure you are. Let me learn from you, love you, savor you, bless you, before you depart. Let me not pass you by in quest of some rare and perfect tomorrow. Let me hold you while I may, for it will not always be so. One day I shall dig my fingers into the earth, or bury my face in the pillow, or stretch my self taut, or raise my hands to the sky, and want all the more for your return.

Mary Jean Irion

Bible Plan

Battle Plan

Fighter Verse:

Prayers

Hospitality/ Outreach

This Week's Memorable Moments

Achievements

Family funnies - Victories - Progress - Promising signs - Small beginnings - Finished projects

Evidences of Grace

Evidence of God's grace - God's mercy - God's faithfulness - God's protection - God's provision

Week of:

Notes

Supplies

Appointments

Marriage is an adventure, like going to war.
G. K. Chesterton

Week of:	We thank Thee that, in the multitude of Thy tender mercies, in the riches of Thy pitiful compassion, Thou hast been pleased to erect this throne of grace, before which we now most humbly bow. We bless Thee that here free favour reigns. *Henry Law*
Bible Plan	
Battle Plan Fighter Verse:	
Prayers	
Hospitality/ Outreach	

This Week's Memorable Moments

Achievements

Family funnies - Victories - Progress - Promising signs - Small beginnings - Finished projects

Evidences of Grace

Evidence of God's grace - God's mercy - God's faithfulness - God's protection - God's provision

Week of:

Notes

Supplies

Appointments

You don't have a soul. You are a Soul. You have a body.
C. S. Lewis

Week of:

The Lord's Day

This is the day which the Lord hath made, we will rejoice and be glad in it. O let our minds be withdrawn from the world, as well as our bodies. Let our retirement be devout. Let our meditation be sweet. Let our conversation be edifying. Let our reading be pious. Let our hearing be profitable—and on Thee may we wait all the day!
William Jay

Bible Plan

Battle Plan

Fighter Verse:

Prayers

Hospitality/ Outreach

This Week's Memorable Moments

Achievements

Family funnies - Victories - Progress - Promising signs - Small beginnings - Finished projects

Evidences of Grace

Evidence of God's grace - God's mercy - God's faithfulness - God's protection - God's provision

Week of:

Notes

Supplies

Appointments

If you live gladly to make others glad in God, your life will be hard, your risks will be high, and your joy will be full.
John Piper

Week of:

The Lord's Day

The Lord will do great things for me, and I will be filled with joy. I will sow in tears, then I will reap with songs of joy. If I go out weeping, Lord, carrying seed to sow, I will return with songs of joy, carrying sheaves with me.
Beth Moore

Bible Plan

Battle Plan

Fighter Verse:

Prayers

Hospitality/ Outreach

This Week's Memorable Moments

Achievements

Family funnies - Victories - Progress - Promising signs - Small beginnings - Finished projects

Evidences of Grace

Evidence of God's grace - God's mercy - God's faithfulness - God's protection - God's provision

Week of:

Notes

Supplies

Appointments

Children are apt to live up to what you believe of them.
Lady Bird Johnson

The Lord's Day

Week of:

"When thou passest through the waters," deep the waves may be and cold,
But Jehovah is our refuge, and His promise is our hold;
For the Lord Himself hath said it, He, the faithful God and true:
"When thou comest to the waters, thou shalt not go down, but THROUGH."
Annie Johnson Flint

Bible Plan

Battle Plan

Fighter Verse:

Prayers

Hospitality/ Outreach

This Week's Memorable Moments

Achievements

Family funnies - Victories - Progress - Promising signs - Small beginnings - Finished projects

Evidences of Grace

Evidence of God's grace - God's mercy - God's faithfulness - God's protection - God's provision

Week of:

Notes

Supplies

Appointments

Women are like teabags; you never know how strong they are until they're put in hot water.
Eleanor Roosevelt

The Lord's Day

Week of:	What is thy season this morning? Is it a season of drought? Then that is the season for showers. Is it a season of great heaviness and black clouds? Then that is the season for showers. "As thy day so shall thy strength be." "I will give thee showers of blessing." The word is in the plural. All kinds of blessings God will send. All God's blessings go together, like links in a golden chain. If He gives converting grace, He will also give comforting grace. He will send "showers of blessings." Look up today, O parched plant, and open thy leaves and flowers for a heavenly watering. *Charles Spurgeon*
Bible Plan	
Battle Plan Fighter Verse:	
Prayers	
Hospitality/ Outreach	

This Week's Memorable Moments

Achievements

Family funnies - Victories - Progress - Promising signs - Small beginnings - Finished projects

Evidences of Grace

Evidence of God's grace - God's mercy - God's faithfulness - God's protection - God's provision

Week of:

Notes

Supplies

Appointments

Often God has to shut a door in our face, so that He can subsequently open the door through which He wants us to go.
Catherine Marshall

Week of:	**The Lord's Day** And while we are the partakers of thy grace, may we be also the dispensers of it too. Freely having received, may we freely give. May we feel it to be the sublimest of all satisfactions, and count it the greatest of all rewards, to save a soul from death, and to hide a multitude of sins. And while endeavouring to do good, may we be prepared to bear evil. May we consider Him who endured the contradiction of sinners against Himself; and if reviled, revile not again; or if opposed or slighted, never grow weary in well doing. *William Jay*
Bible Plan	
Battle Plan Fighter Verse:	
Prayers	
Hospitality/ Outreach	

This Week's Memorable Moments

Achievements

Family funnies - Victories - Progress - Promising signs - Small beginnings - Finished projects

Evidences of Grace

Evidence of God's grace - God's mercy - God's faithfulness - God's protection - God's provision

Week of:

Notes

Supplies

Appointments

Good teachers are those who know how little they know. Bad teachers are those who think they know more than they don't know.
R. Verdi

Week of:

When I have learnt to love God better than my earthly dearest, I shall love my earthly dearest better than I do now. In so far as I learn to love my earthly dearest at the expense of God and *instead* of God, I shall be moving towards the state in which I shall not love my earthly dearest at all. When first things are put first, second things are not suppressed but increased.

C. S. Lewis

Bible Plan

Battle Plan

Fighter Verse:

Prayers

Hospitality/ Outreach

This Week's Memorable Moments

Achievements

Family funnies - Victories - Progress - Promising signs - Small beginnings - Finished projects

Evidences of Grace

Evidence of God's grace - God's mercy - God's faithfulness - God's protection - God's provision

Week of:

Notes

Supplies

Appointments

A room without books is like a body without a soul.

Marcus Julius Cicero

Week of:	Teach me Your way, O Lord, and I will walk in Your truth. Give me an undivided heart that I may fear Your name. Do not allow anything to snatch the word of truth from my mouth, O Lord, for I have put my hope in Your laws. Beth Moore
Bible Plan	
Battle Plan Fighter Verse:	
Prayers	
Hospitality/ Outreach	

This Week's Memorable Moments	Achievements

Family funnies - Victories - Progress - Promising signs - Small beginnings - Finished projects

Evidences of Grace

Evidence of God's grace - God's mercy - God's faithfulness - God's protection - God's provision

Week of:

Notes

Supplies

Appointments

In science we have been reading only the notes to a poem; in Christianity we find the poem itself.
C. S. Lewis

Week of:

The Lord's Day

'Tis heaven on earth to taste his love,
To feel his quickening grace;
And all the Heaven I hope above
Is but to see his face.
Isaac Watts

Bible Plan

Battle Plan

Fighter Verse:

Prayers

Hospitality/ Outreach

This Week's Memorable Moments	Achievements

Family funnies - Victories - Progress - Promising signs - Small beginnings - Finished projects

Evidences of Grace

Evidence of God's grace - God's mercy - God's faithfulness - God's protection - God's provision

Week of:

Notes

Supplies

Appointments

The strength of patience hangs on our capacity to believe that God is up to something good for us in all our delays and detours.
John Piper

Week of:	**The Lord's Day** The heavens are high above the earth, but greater far are Thy mercies to usward. We cannot count the stars which bespangle the canopy of the skies, or the sands which begird the seas, or the drops which compose the ocean's boundlessness, but all these are finite, while infinity is the only measure of Thy grace. *Henry Law*
Bible Plan	
Battle Plan Fighter Verse:	
Prayers	
Hospitality/ Outreach	

This Week's Memorable Moments

Achievements

Family funnies - Victories - Progress - Promising signs - Small beginnings - Finished projects

Evidences of Grace

Evidence of God's grace - God's mercy - God's faithfulness - God's protection - God's provision

Week of:

Notes

Supplies

Appointments

If you can't explain it to a six-year-old, you don't understand it yourself.
Albert Einstein

Week of:

Batter my heart, three-person'd God, for you
As yet but knock, breathe, shine, and seek to mend;
That I may rise and stand, o'erthrow me and bend
Your force to break, blow, burn, and make me new.
John Donne

Bible Plan

Battle Plan

Fighter Verse:

Prayers

Hospitality/ Outreach

This Week's Memorable Moments	Achievements

Family funnies - Victories - Progress - Promising signs - Small beginnings - Finished projects

Evidences of Grace

Evidence of God's grace - God's mercy - God's faithfulness - God's protection - God's provision

Week of:

Notes

Supplies

Appointments

There is nothing better than a friend, unless it is a friend with chocolate.
Charles Dickens

Week of:

The Lord's Day

My God, how wonderful Thou art,
Thy majesty how bright!
How beautiful Thy mercy-seat,
In depth of burning light.
Frederick W. Faber

Bible Plan

Battle Plan

Fighter Verse:

Prayers

Hospitality/ Outreach

This Week's Memorable Moments

Achievements

Family funnies - Victories - Progress - Promising signs - Small beginnings - Finished projects

Evidences of Grace

Evidence of God's grace - God's mercy - God's faithfulness - God's protection - God's provision

Week of:

Notes

Supplies

Appointments

I suppose it is because nearly all children go to school nowadays and have things arranged for them that they seem so forlornly unable to produce their own ideas in holiday time.
Agatha Christie

Week of:	**The Lord's Day** Lord Jesus Christ, may You and God, my Father, who loves me and by His grace gave me eternal encouragement and good hope, encourage my heart and strengthen me in every good deed and word. *Beth Moore*
Bible Plan	
Battle Plan Fighter Verse:	
Prayers	
Hospitality/ Outreach	

This Week's Memorable Moments	Achievements

Family funnies - Victories - Progress - Promising signs - Small beginnings - Finished projects

Evidences of Grace

Evidence of God's grace - God's mercy - God's faithfulness - God's protection - God's provision

Week of:

Notes

Supplies

Appointments

A characteristic of the normal child is he doesn't act that way very often.

Franklin P. Jones

Week of:	**The Lord's Day** O Truthful God, let me receive the happiness of heaven which You promise so that my joy may be full. In the meantime, let my mind think of it, let my tongue talk of it, let my heart long for it, let my mouth speak of it, let my soul hunger after it, let my flesh thirst after it, let my whole being desire it. St. Augustine
Bible Plan	
Battle Plan Fighter Verse:	
Prayers	
Hospitality/ Outreach	

This Week's Memorable Moments

Achievements

Family funnies - Victories - Progress - Promising signs - Small beginnings - Finished projects

Evidences of Grace

Evidence of God's grace - God's mercy - God's faithfulness - God's protection - God's provision

Week of:

Notes

Supplies

Appointments

Each day of our lives we make deposits in the memory banks of our children.
Charles R. Swindoll

Week of:	Help us this day, O Lord to serve Thee devoutly and the world busily. May we do our work wisely, go to meat appetitely, sit thereafter discreetly, arise temperately, please our friends duly, go to bed merrily and sleep surely—all in the joy of our Lord and Saviour, Jesus Christ. *Traditional, Middle Ages*
Bible Plan	
Battle Plan Fighter Verse:	
Prayers	
Hospitality/ Outreach	

This Week's Memorable Moments

Achievements

Family funnies - Victories - Progress - Promising signs - Small beginnings - Finished projects

Evidences of Grace

Evidence of God's grace - God's mercy - God's faithfulness - God's protection - God's provision

Week of:

Notes

Supplies

Appointments

Having a family is like having a bowling alley installed in your brain.
Martin Mull

Week of:	**The Lord's Day** Have mercy on me, O God, according to your unfailing love; according to your great compassion blot out my transgressions. Wash away all my iniquity and cleanse me from my sin. . . . Create in me a pure heart, O God, and renew a steadfast spirit within me. Do not cast me from your presence or take your Holy Spirit from me. Restore to me the joy of your salvation and grant me a willing spirit, to sustain me. Psalm 51:1–2; 10–12
Bible Plan	
Battle Plan Fighter Verse:	
Prayers	
Hospitality/ Outreach	

This Week's Memorable Moments

Achievements

Family funnies - Victories - Progress - Promising signs - Small beginnings - Finished projects

Evidences of Grace

Evidence of God's grace - God's mercy - God's faithfulness - God's protection - God's provision

Week of:

Notes

Supplies

Appointments

There is always one moment in childhood when the door opens and lets the future in.
Graham Greene

Week of:

"He knoweth our frame; he remembereth that we are dust." Think of that when you are tempted to question the gentleness of His leading. He is remembering all the time; and not one step will He make you take beyond what your foot is able to endure. Never mind if you think it will not be able for the step that seems to come next; either He will so strengthen it that it shall be able, or He will call a sudden halt, and you shall not have to take it at all.

Frances Ridley Havergal

Bible Plan

Battle Plan

Fighter Verse:

Prayers

Hospitality/ Outreach

This Week's Memorable Moments	Achievements

Family funnies - Victories - Progress - Promising signs - Small beginnings - Finished projects

Evidences of Grace

Evidence of God's grace - God's mercy - God's faithfulness - God's protection - God's provision

Week of:

Notes

Supplies

Appointments

Few things are more satisfying than seeing your own children have teenagers of their own.
Doug Larson

Week of:	There must be a beginning of any great matter, but the continuing unto the end until it be thoroughly finished yields the true glory. *Sir Francis Drake*
Bible Plan	
Battle Plan Fighter Verse:	
Prayers	
Hospitality/ Outreach	

This Week's Memorable Moments

Achievements

Family funnies - Victories - Progress - Promising signs - Small beginnings - Finished projects

Evidences of Grace

Evidence of God's grace - God's mercy - God's faithfulness - God's protection - God's provision

Week of:

Notes

Supplies

Appointments

Acceptance says, "True, this is my situation at the moment. I'll look unblinkingly at the reality of it. But I'll also open my hands to accept willingly whatever a loving Father sends me."
Catherine Marshall

Week of:

The Lord's Day

To him who is able to keep you from stumbling and to present you before his glorious presence without fault and with great joy—to the only God our Savior be glory, majesty, power and authority, through Jesus Christ our Lord, before all ages, now and forevermore! Amen.
Jude 1:24–25

Bible Plan

Battle Plan

Fighter Verse:

Prayers

Hospitality/ Outreach

This Week's Memorable Moments

Achievements

Family funnies - Victories - Progress - Promising signs - Small beginnings - Finished projects

Evidences of Grace

Evidence of God's grace - God's mercy - God's faithfulness - God's protection - God's provision

Week of:

Notes

Supplies

Appointments

The fact that I am a woman does not make me a different kind of Christian, but the fact that I am a Christian does make me a different kind of woman.
Elisabeth Elliot

Week of:	And shall I pray, Oh, change Thy will, my Father, Until it be according unto mine? Ah no, Lord, no, that never could be, rather I pray Thee, Blend my human will with Thine. Amy Carmichael
Bible Plan	
Battle Plan Fighter Verse:	
Prayers	
Hospitality/ Outreach	

This Week's Memorable Moments

Achievements

Family funnies - Victories - Progress - Promising signs - Small beginnings - Finished projects

Evidences of Grace

Evidence of God's grace - God's mercy - God's faithfulness - God's protection - God's provision

Week of:

Notes

Supplies

Appointments

Keep your love for one another at full strength, because love covers a multitude of sins.
1 Peter 4:8, HCSB

Week of:	**The Lord's Day** If any one would tell you the shortest, surest way to all happiness, and all perfection, he must tell you to make it a rule to yourself, to thank and praise God for everything that happens to you. For it is certain, that whatever seeming calamity happens to you, if you thank and praise God for it, you turn it into a blessing. William Law
Bible Plan	
Battle Plan Fighter Verse:	
Prayers	
Hospitality/ Outreach	

This Week's Memorable Moments

Achievements

Family funnies - Victories - Progress - Promising signs - Small beginnings - Finished projects

Evidences of Grace

Evidence of God's grace - God's mercy - God's faithfulness - God's protection - God's provision

Week of:

Notes

Supplies

Appointments

I would go to the deeps a hundred times to cheer a downcast spirit; it is good for me to have been afflicted, that I might know how to speak a word in season to one that is weary.
Charles Spurgeon

Week of:	"Remember the word unto thy servant, on which thou hast caused me to hope," is most prevalent pleading. It is a double argument: it is Thy Word. Wilt Thou not keep it? Why hast thou spoken of it, if Thou wilt not make it good? Thou hast caused me to hope in it, wilt Thou disappoint the hope which Thou has Thyself begotten in me? Charles Spurgeon
Bible Plan	
Battle Plan Fighter Verse:	
Prayers	
Hospitality/ Outreach	

This Week's Memorable Moments | Achievements

Family funnies - Victories - Progress - Promising signs - Small beginnings - Finished projects

Evidences of Grace

Evidence of God's grace - God's mercy - God's faithfulness - God's protection - God's provision

Week of:

Notes

Supplies

Appointments

A woman uses her intelligence to find reasons to support her intuition.
G. K. Chesterton

Week of:

It lies with each of us to choose which they shall be. It all depends, not upon what these events are, but upon how we take them. If we lie down under them, and let them roll over us and crush us, they become Juggernaut cars, but if we climb up into them, as into a car of victory, and make them carry us triumphantly onward and upward, they become the chariots of God.
Hannah Whitall Smith

Bible Plan

Battle Plan

Fighter Verse:

Prayers

Hospitality/ Outreach

This Week's Memorable Moments

Achievements

Family funnies - Victories - Progress - Promising signs - Small beginnings - Finished projects

Evidences of Grace

Evidence of God's grace - God's mercy - God's faithfulness - God's protection - God's provision

Week of:

Notes

Supplies

Appointments

Love is not affectionate feeling, but a steady wish for the loved person's ultimate good as far as it can be obtained.
C. S. Lewis

Week of:

Knowing God without knowing our own wretchedness makes for pride. Knowing our wretchedness without knowing God makes for despair. Knowing Jesus Christ strikes the balance because he shows us both God and our own wretchedness.
Blaise Pascal

Bible Plan

Battle Plan

Fighter Verse:

Prayers

Hospitality/ Outreach

This Week's Memorable Moments

Achievements

Family funnies - Victories - Progress - Promising signs - Small beginnings - Finished projects

Evidences of Grace

Evidence of God's grace - God's mercy - God's faithfulness - God's protection - God's provision

Week of:

Notes

Supplies

Appointments

Grace is the pleasure of God to magnify the worth of God by giving sinners the right and power to delight in God without obscuring the glory of God.
John Piper

Week of:

The Lord's Day

The awful thing is that beauty is mysterious as well as terrible. God and the devil are fighting there, and the battlefield is the heart of man.
Fyodor Dostoyevsky

Bible Plan

Battle Plan

Fighter Verse:

Prayers

Hospitality/ Outreach

This Week's Memorable Moments

Achievements

Family funnies - Victories - Progress - Promising signs - Small beginnings - Finished projects

Evidences of Grace

Evidence of God's grace - God's mercy - God's faithfulness - God's protection - God's provision

Week of:

Notes

Supplies

Appointments

If you want your children to be intelligent, read them fairy tales. If you want them to be more intelligent, read them more fairy tales.
Albert Einstein

Week of:

The Lord's Day

The world is charged with the grandeur of God.
It will flame out, like shining from shook foil;
It gathers to a greatness, like the ooze of oil
Crushed. . . .
Because the Holy Ghost over the bent world broods with warm breast and ah! bright wings.
Gerard Manley Hopkins

Bible Plan

Battle Plan

Fighter Verse:

Prayers

Hospitality/ Outreach

This Week's Memorable Moments

Achievements

Family funnies - Victories - Progress - Promising signs - Small beginnings - Finished projects

Evidences of Grace

Evidence of God's grace - God's mercy - God's faithfulness - God's protection - God's provision

Week of:

Notes

Supplies

Appointments

Wisdom begins in wonder.
Socrates

Week of:	**The Lord's Day** To have found God and still to pursue Him is the soul's paradox of love, scorned indeed by the too-easily-satisfied religionist, but justified in happy experience by the children of the burning heart. A. W. Tozer
Bible Plan	
Battle Plan Fighter Verse:	
Prayers	
Hospitality/ Outreach	

This Week's Memorable Moments

Achievements

Family funnies - Victories - Progress - Promising signs - Small beginnings - Finished projects

Evidences of Grace

Evidence of God's grace - God's mercy - God's faithfulness - God's protection - God's provision

Week of:

Notes

Supplies

Appointments

There are perhaps no days of our childhood we lived so fully as those we believe we let slip by without having lived them, those we spent with a favorite book.
Marcel Proust

Week of:	He is the God of boundless resources. The only limit is in us. Our asking, our thinking, our praying are too small; our expectations are too limited. He is trying to lift us up to a higher conception, and lure us on to a mightier expectation and appropriation. Oh, shall we put Him in derision? There is no limit to what we may ask and expect of our glorious El-Shaddai; and there is but one measure here given for His blessing, and that is "according to the power that worketh in us." A. B. Simpson
Bible Plan	
Battle Plan Fighter Verse:	
Prayers	
Hospitality/ Outreach	

This Week's Memorable Moments

Achievements

Family funnies - Victories - Progress - Promising signs - Small beginnings - Finished projects

Evidences of Grace

Evidence of God's grace - God's mercy - God's faithfulness - God's protection - God's provision

Week of:

Notes

Supplies

Appointments

You know children are growing up when they start asking questions that have answers.
John Plomp

Week of:	God created us for this: to live our lives in a way that makes him look more like the greatness and the beauty and the infinite worth that he really is. This is what it means to be created in the image of God. *John Piper*
Bible Plan	
Battle Plan Fighter Verse:	
Prayers	
Hospitality/ Outreach	

This Week's Memorable Moments	Achievements

Family funnies - Victories - Progress - Promising signs - Small beginnings - Finished projects

Evidences of Grace

Evidence of God's grace - God's mercy - God's faithfulness - God's protection - God's provision

Week of:

Notes

Supplies

Appointments

Even when freshly washed and relieved of all obvious confections, children tend to be sticky.
Fran Lebowitz

Week of:

Father, hear us, we are praying. Hear the words our hearts are saying. We are praying for our children. . . . Through life's troubled waters steer them, through life's bitter battle cheer them, Father, Father, be Thou near them. . . . And wherever they may bide, lead them home at eventide.

Amy Carmichael

Bible Plan

Battle Plan

Fighter Verse:

Prayers

Hospitality/ Outreach

This Week's Memorable Moments

Achievements

Family funnies - Victories - Progress - Promising signs - Small beginnings - Finished projects

Evidences of Grace

Evidence of God's grace - God's mercy - God's faithfulness - God's protection - God's provision

Week of:

Notes

Supplies

Appointments

The prime purpose of being four is to enjoy being four—of secondary importance is to prepare for being five.
Jim Trelease

Week of:

Our Father, come and give rest to your children now. Take the helmet from our brow, remove from us the weight of our heavy armor for awhile, and may we just have peace, perfect peace, and be at rest. Oh! help us, we pray You, now.
Charles Spurgeon

Bible Plan

Battle Plan

Fighter Verse:

Prayers

Hospitality/ Outreach

This Week's Memorable Moments

Achievements

Family funnies - Victories - Progress - Promising signs - Small beginnings - Finished projects

Evidences of Grace

Evidence of God's grace - God's mercy - God's faithfulness - God's protection - God's provision

Week of:

Notes

Supplies

Appointments

Cleaning your house while your kids are still growing up is like shoveling the walk before it stops snowing.
Phyllis Diller

Week of:	Late have I loved you, O Beauty ever ancient, ever new, late have I loved you! You were within me, but I was outside, and it was there that I searched for you. In my unloveliness I plunged into the lovely things which you created. You were with me, but I was not with you. Created things kept me from you; yet if they had not been in you they would not have been at all. You called, you shouted, and you broke through my deafness. You flashed, you shone, and you dispelled my blindness. You breathed your fragrance on me; I drew in breath and now I pant for you. I have tasted you, now I hunger and thirst for more. You touched me, and I burned for your peace. St. Augustine
Bible Plan	
Battle Plan Fighter Verse:	
Prayers	
Hospitality/ Outreach	

This Week's Memorable Moments

Achievements

Family funnies - Victories - Progress - Promising signs - Small beginnings - Finished projects

Evidences of Grace

Evidence of God's grace - God's mercy - God's faithfulness - God's protection - God's provision

Week of:

Notes

Supplies

Appointments

My theory on housework is, if the item doesn't multiply, smell, catch on fire or block the refrigerator door, let it be. No one cares. Why should you?
Erma Bombeck

Week of:

Be thou my vision, O Lord of my heart,
Naught be all else to me save that thou art;
Thou my best thought, by day or by night,
Waking or sleeping thy presence my light.
Gaelic hymn

Bible Plan

Battle Plan

Fighter Verse:

Prayers

Hospitality/ Outreach

This Week's Memorable Moments

Achievements

Family funnies - Victories - Progress - Promising signs - Small beginnings - Finished projects

Evidences of Grace

Evidence of God's grace - God's mercy - God's faithfulness - God's protection - God's provision

Week of:

Notes

Supplies

Appointments

The children must enjoy the book. The ideas it holds must each make that sudden, delightful impact upon their minds, must cause that intellectual stir, which mark the inception of an idea.
Charlotte Mason

Week of:

Glory be to God for dappled things—For skies of couple-colour as a brinded cow; for rose-moles all in stipple upon trout that swim; fresh-firecoal chestnut-falls; finches' wings;
Landscape plotted and pieced—fold, fallow and plough; and all trades, their gear and tackle and trim.
All things counter, original, spare, strange; whatever is fickle, freckled (who knows how?)
With swift, slow; sweet, sour; adazzle, dim;
He fathers-forth whose beauty is past change. Praise him.
Gerard Manley Hopkins

Bible Plan

Battle Plan

Fighter Verse:

Prayers

Hospitality/ Outreach

This Week's Memorable Moments

Achievements

Family funnies - Victories - Progress - Promising signs - Small beginnings - Finished projects

Evidences of Grace

Evidence of God's grace - God's mercy - God's faithfulness - God's protection - God's provision

Week of:

Notes

Supplies

Appointments

Let your religion be less of a theory and more of a love affair.
G. K. Chesterton

Week of:

Behold, Lord, an empty vessel that needs to be filled.
My Lord, fill it.
I am weak in the faith; strengthen me. I am cold in love; warm me and make me fervent, that my love may go out to my neighbor. I do not have a strong and firm faith; at times I doubt and am unable to trust You altogether.
O Lord, help me. Strengthen my faith and trust in You.
In You I have sealed the treasure of all I have.
Martin Luther

Bible Plan

Battle Plan

Fighter Verse:

Prayers

Hospitality/ Outreach

This Week's Memorable Moments

Achievements

Family funnies - Victories - Progress - Promising signs - Small beginnings - Finished projects

Evidences of Grace

Evidence of God's grace - God's mercy - God's faithfulness - God's protection - God's provision

Week of:

Notes

Supplies

Appointments

One of the great uses of Twitter and Facebook will be to prove at the Last Day that prayerlessness was not from lack of time.
John Piper

Week of:	**The Lord's Day** O worship the Lord in the beauty of holiness! Bow down before Hm, His glory proclaim; With gold of obedience, and incense of lowliness, Kneel and adore Him, the Lord is His name! J. S. B. Monsell
Bible Plan	
Battle Plan Fighter Verse:	
Prayers	
Hospitality/ Outreach	

This Week's Memorable Moments

Achievements

Family funnies - Victories - Progress - Promising signs - Small beginnings - Finished projects

Evidences of Grace

Evidence of God's grace - God's mercy - God's faithfulness - God's protection - God's provision

Week of:

Notes

Supplies

Appointments

There's nothing that can help you understand your beliefs more than trying to explain them to an inquisitive child.
Frank A. Clark

Week of:

The Lord's Day

Come, let us sing for joy to the LORD; let us shout aloud to the Rock of our salvation. Let us come before him with thanksgiving and extol him with music and song. For the LORD is the great God, the great King above all gods. In his hand are the depths of the earth, and the mountain peaks belong to him. The sea is his, for he made it, and his hands formed the dry land. Come, let us bow down in worship, let us kneel before the LORD our Maker; for he is our God and we are the people of his pasture, the flock under his care.
Psalm. 95:1–7

Bible Plan

Battle Plan

Fighter Verse:

Prayers

Hospitality/ Outreach

This Week's Memorable Moments

Achievements

Family funnies - Victories - Progress - Promising signs - Small beginnings - Finished projects

Evidences of Grace

Evidence of God's grace - God's mercy - God's faithfulness - God's protection - God's provision

Week of:

Notes

Supplies

Appointments

What is most important and valuable about the home as a base for children's growth into the world is not that it is a better school than the schools, but that it isn't a school at all.
John Holt

Week of:	Of all the creatures both in sea and land, Only to man thou hast made known thy ways, And put the pen alone into his hand. And made him secretary of thy praise. *George Herbert*
Bible Plan	
Battle Plan Fighter Verse:	
Prayers	
Hospitality/ Outreach	

This Week's Memorable Moments	Achievements

Family funnies - Victories - Progress - Promising signs - Small beginnings - Finished projects

Evidences of Grace

Evidence of God's grace - God's mercy - God's faithfulness - God's protection - God's provision

Week of:

Notes

Supplies

Appointments

Thank goodness, my education was neglected.
Beatrix Potter

Week of:

Many duties are before us. Our callings demand firmness, energy, and zeal. We desire to work in Thy vineyard this day, not slothful in any business, but as Thy servants, devoted to Thy cause, valiant in Thy name. We know that love is the working grace, and that our love will be commensurate with our faith. Let but our faith stride forth in giant-power, and love will respond and put energy into every act, and then at the close of this day, Thy Spirit will bear witness with our spirit: well done, good and faithful servant. Oh! then receive our cry, increase our faith.

Henry Law

Bible Plan

Battle Plan

Fighter Verse:

Prayers

Hospitality/ Outreach

This Week's Memorable Moments

Achievements

Family funnies - Victories - Progress - Promising signs - Small beginnings - Finished projects

Evidences of Grace

Evidence of God's grace - God's mercy - God's faithfulness - God's protection - God's provision

Week of:

Notes

Supplies

Appointments

Education is what remains after one has forgotten everything he learned in school.
attributed to Albert Einstein

The Lord's Day

Week of:

You, my God, are supreme, utmost in goodness, mightiest and all-powerful, most merciful and most just. You are the most hidden from us and yet the most present amongst us, the most beautiful and yet the most strong, ever enduring and yet we cannot comprehend you. You are unchangeable and yet you change all things. You are never new, never old, and yet all things have new life from you.
St. Augustine

Bible Plan

Battle Plan

Fighter Verse:

Prayers

Hospitality/ Outreach

This Week's Memorable Moments

Achievements

Family funnies - Victories - Progress - Promising signs - Small beginnings - Finished projects

Evidences of Grace

Evidence of God's grace - God's mercy - God's faithfulness - God's protection - God's provision

Week of:

Notes

Supplies

Appointments

What we want is to see the child in pursuit of knowledge, and not knowledge in pursuit of the child.
George Bernard Shaw

Week of:	## The Lord's Day God cannot endure that unfestive, mirthless attitude of ours in which we eat our bread in sorrow, with pretentious, busy haste, or even with shame. Through our daily meals He is calling us to rejoice, to keep holiday in the midst of our working day. *Dietrich Bonhoeffer*
Bible Plan	
Battle Plan Fighter Verse:	
Prayers	
Hospitality/ Outreach	

This Week's Memorable Moments | Achievements

Family funnies - Victories - Progress - Promising signs - Small beginnings - Finished projects

Evidences of Grace

Evidence of God's grace - God's mercy - God's faithfulness - God's protection - God's provision

Week of:

Notes

Supplies

Appointments

True contentment is a real and even an active virtue; it is not only affirmative but creative. . . . It is the power of getting out of any situation all there is in it.
G. K. Chesterton

Week of:	The Lord's Day If I am a son of God, nothing but God will satisfy my soul; no amount of comfort, no amount of ease, no amount of pleasure, will give me peace or rest. If I had the full cup of all the world's joys held up to me, and could drain it to the dregs, I should still remain thirsty if I had not God. *G. Geoffrey Studdert Kennedy*
Bible Plan	
Battle Plan Fighter Verse:	
Prayers	
Hospitality/ Outreach	

This Week's Memorable Moments

Achievements

Family funnies - Victories - Progress - Promising signs - Small beginnings - Finished projects

Evidences of Grace

Evidence of God's grace - God's mercy - God's faithfulness - God's protection - God's provision

Week of:

Notes

Supplies

Appointments

Why do we say no? In order to say yes to what really matters.
Miriam Adeney

Week of:	The Lord's Day You say, "If I had a little more, I should be very satisfied." You make a mistake. If you are not content with what you have, you would not be satisfied if it were doubled. Charles Spurgeon
Bible Plan	
Battle Plan Fighter Verse:	
Prayers	
Hospitality/ Outreach	

This Week's Memorable Moments | Achievements

Family funnies - Victories - Progress - Promising signs - Small beginnings - Finished projects

Evidences of Grace

Evidence of God's grace - God's mercy - God's faithfulness - God's protection - God's provision

Week of:

Notes

Supplies

Appointments

Fear knocked at the door. Faith answered. No one was there.
Traditional

Week of:	The Lord's Day Forgiveness is the key that unlocks the door of resentment and the handcuffs of hate. It is a power that breaks the chains of bitterness and the shackles of selfishness. *Corrie ten Boom*
Bible Plan	
Battle Plan Fighter Verse:	
Prayers	
Hospitality/ Outreach	

This Week's Memorable Moments

Achievements

Family funnies - Victories - Progress - Promising signs - Small beginnings - Finished projects

Evidences of Grace

Evidence of God's grace - God's mercy - God's faithfulness - God's protection - God's provision

Week of:

Notes

Supplies

Appointments

Eternal life is not a life for the future. By charity we start eternity right here below.

Henri de Lubac

Student	Scores								Total

Student	Scores								Total

Student	Scores								Total

Student	Scores								Total

Student	Scores								Total

Student	Scores								Total

Student

READING LIST

Title	Author	Type

Student

READING LIST

Title	Author	Type

A = ASSIGNED **I** = INDEPENDENT **N** = NONFICTION **F** = FICTION

Student

READING LIST

Title	Author	Type

Student

READING LIST

Title	Author	Type

A = ASSIGNED **I** = INDEPENDENT **N** = NONFICTION **F** = FICTION

Student

READING LIST

Title	Author	Type

Student

READING LIST

Title	Author	Type

A = ASSIGNED **I** = INDEPENDENT **N** = NONFICTION **F** = FICTION

Student	Student
Field Trips - Outside Activities	Field Trips - Outside Activities

Student	Student
Field Trips - Outside Activities	Field Trips - Outside Activities

Student	Student
Field Trips - Outside Activities	Field Trips - Outside Activities

Checklist for Raising an Independent Learner

- Give kids a choice whenever possible. For example, allow young children to choose between two possible books to read, or invite teenagers to attend the curriculum fair with you and help choose their course of study.

- Give kids plenty of leisure time for critical thinking. Allow them to ponder and wonder. Encourage them to keep a journal of their intellectual life.

- Value imagination and play. Your children's imaginative life inoculates against the effects of stress and also provides the seedbed for critical thinking as they mature.

- Let kids manage chunks of their own time. For example, permit younger children to choose the order in which they complete their assigned activities before lunch. Give older kids the freedom to decide when to complete their assignments each week.

- Provide regular, targeted feedback. Students lose motivation when they do not have an accurate sense of their achievement. Touch base daily with young children about their progress. Communicate at least once a week with teens. In skill areas, the more specific and timely the feedback, the more students will be able to manage their own progress.

- Allow your kids to initiate projects and writing of their own choosing. Initiative is your friend. You won't survive homeschooling in the long run without self-motivated students.

- Learn to facilitate, not dictate. Provide the guidelines (e.g., budget constraints, deadlines, etc.) and tools necessary to help your children reach their goals. Then assist them in the process.

- Focus on the three P's: Projects, Papers, and Performances. These types of assignments help kids develop skills for independent learning, think more critically, and produce work they won't want to throw away (unlike those worksheets.)

- Don't tackle a project or subject of study until your child is ready to do the majority of the work.

- Model independent learning. Keep the gift of curiosity alive in yourself. Talk with your kids about your own stack of library books or your latest topic of inquiry.

- Interest indicates readiness. Age is really not a good indicator of readiness, but interest is. When your child is already motivated to pursue a line of inquiry or acquire a skill, that's the time to start. Go with the momentum. It might not be there later.

- Effort produces success; success produces persistence. Don't let your child quit an activity just because it's hard. Discern first if his problem stems from being overly challenged—that is, your child is making a lot of effort, but developmentally isn't ready for the task. In that case, adjustment is necessary. But pressing through challenge builds self-confidence for learning. Thank God for the opportunity and throw your weight into the project, too.

- Use discovery learning—that means giving kids time to mess around and experiment with stuff so they can discover the underlying concepts and principles themselves. Ask your children thought-provoking questions, but don't provide the answers. Instead, allow them to puzzle out the solutions on their own.

- Take time for your child's questions. Raising questions is a brain-building strategy that emerges as soon as kids can talk and then is often quenched because classroom teachers have an agenda to stick to. But you have the time for these, and your agenda should be "What's this kid ready and interested in learning?" instead of "I have a curriculum I have to get through by the end of the year." Let the questions your child asks direct your study. Write them down. Show they are important. Look up the answers together on the Internet or at the library.

- Let your children teach. In any given educational setting, it's the teacher who learns the most. So leverage that advantage by allowing your kids to share with the whole family what they have learned on their own. Or give your older children specific responsibilities for teaching younger children. Figuring out how to explain an idea or skill will deepen the child's understanding.

Motivating the Reluctant Learner

- All kids are reluctant or resistant at some point in any homeschool program. When this happens, your question should not be "How can I teach this child this stuff?" but rather "How can I motivate this child to learn this stuff?"

- Children learn only when they are cognitively engaged. They need to expend effort for that to happen. So motivation is not optional.

- Is your child developmentally ready for a particular task or topic? Conventional schools have created an arbitrary scope and sequence they expect kids to follow because they are mass educating. But God has given each child an inner timetable according to His design.

- Are there stressors in the environment affecting your child's motivation? These could include conflict with another sibling or even tension between you and another child. Is your reluctant learner worried about something?

- Are you honoring your child's learning style? See the next section (page 270) for a brief description of different types of learners; see also chapter nine of *The Ultimate Guide to Homeschooling* for a full elaboration.

- Reevaluate your methods. What approach are you taking to the problematic topic or task? Would this subject work better in a co-op setting? Or first thing in the morning? Is your child getting enough assistance when things get difficult or confusing?

- Reevaluate your resources. First ask yourself, "Would I find this subject interesting if I had to use this curriculum?" If you can't stay engaged, it's likely your child won't be able to either.

- Add timely accountability. Deadlines, assessment, and targeted feedback are all important components necessary to maintaining motivation. Think about the role a good coach plays in helping an athlete train. That's a good metaphor for what good teachers do to help students stay motivated.

- Try rewards (cautiously). Research has found that rewards can actually undermine internal motivation. But where kids have no inner drive to learn a subject, external incentives may be necessary. Rewards should be carefully selected and a clear measurement given for how they are to be earned. (There is a fine line between incentivizing and bribing. If you figure out where that is, let me know.)

- Add outside influences. As our kids get older, they will desire to broaden their circle of influence. This is an important stepping stone toward adulthood. You can use this desire strategically to aid in learning as well. For instance, perhaps a mentor or tutor in a particular subject area will help provide motivation. Or you might consider studying the topic in a small group with highly motivated peers.

- Add competition. Remember, these are all just tips, and I'm not suggesting all of these will work well with all kids. Competition can be very motivating for certain types of students, and the nature of that competition can vary. For instance, many children will find it motivating to merely compete against themselves to see if they can better their scores in a subject area. Some educational software uses this format. Other students will enthusiastically study for an academic competition. For example, many debate teams, geography and spelling bees, math leagues, etc., encourage homeschoolers to participate.

- Persist. Remember Winston Churchill's exhortation: "Never, never, never give up!" If quitting isn't an option and your kids know that is your stance, the tide will eventually turn in your favor.

Learning Styles and Thinking Skills

IDENTIFY YOUR CHILD'S LEARNING STYLE

Type A: (Actual-Spontaneous Learner)	
must do to learn autonomous flexible risk-taker competitive	inventive outgoing seeks adventure and variety short attention span does not like boundaries impulsive

Type B: (Actual-Routine Learner)	
methodical likes rules, routine and tradition compliant desires your approval thoughtful and helpful	a nurturer by nature dependable not flexible not inventive feeler

Type C: (Conceptual-Specific Learner)	
serious-minded inquisitive satisfied being alone independent learner strong powers of concentration	focused interest easily frustrated perfectionistic detail-oriented thinker mathematical

Type D: (Conceptual-Global Learner)	
thinks big picture creative interested in people enjoys groups outgoing	verbal peacemaker ambitious intuitive forgetful careless

Learning Styles Inventory (Golay, 1982)
You will find tips for teaching to your child's learning style in chapter 9 of *The Ultimate Guide to Homeschooling* (Apologia, 2009).

Bloom's Taxonomy of Thinking Skills
When children use higher levels of thinking (i.e., analysis, synthesis, or evaluation) to learn, what they learn is stored in long-term memory and therefore readily recalled.

Knowledge	I remember, I know, I recall, I define, I name, I recognize, I memorize, I repeat, I identify, I list
Comprehension	I understand, I summarize, I explain, I reword, I exemplify, I discuss, I describe, I draw, I match
Application	I use what I know, I research, I demonstrate how, I solve a problem, I perform, I organize, I practice, I calculate, I operate
Analysis	I break down information, I compare and contrast, I note relationships, I categorize, I explain cause and effect, I deduce, I investigate, I experiment, I classify, I discriminate, I probe
Evaluation	I form and support opinions, I justify, I recommend, I predict, I critique, I appraise, I conclude, I choose, I argue, I estimate, I consider
Synthesis	I use what I know to create something new, I plan, I infer, I propose, I invent, I write, I compose, I collect, I modify, I formulate, I arrange, I design, I construct, I generalize

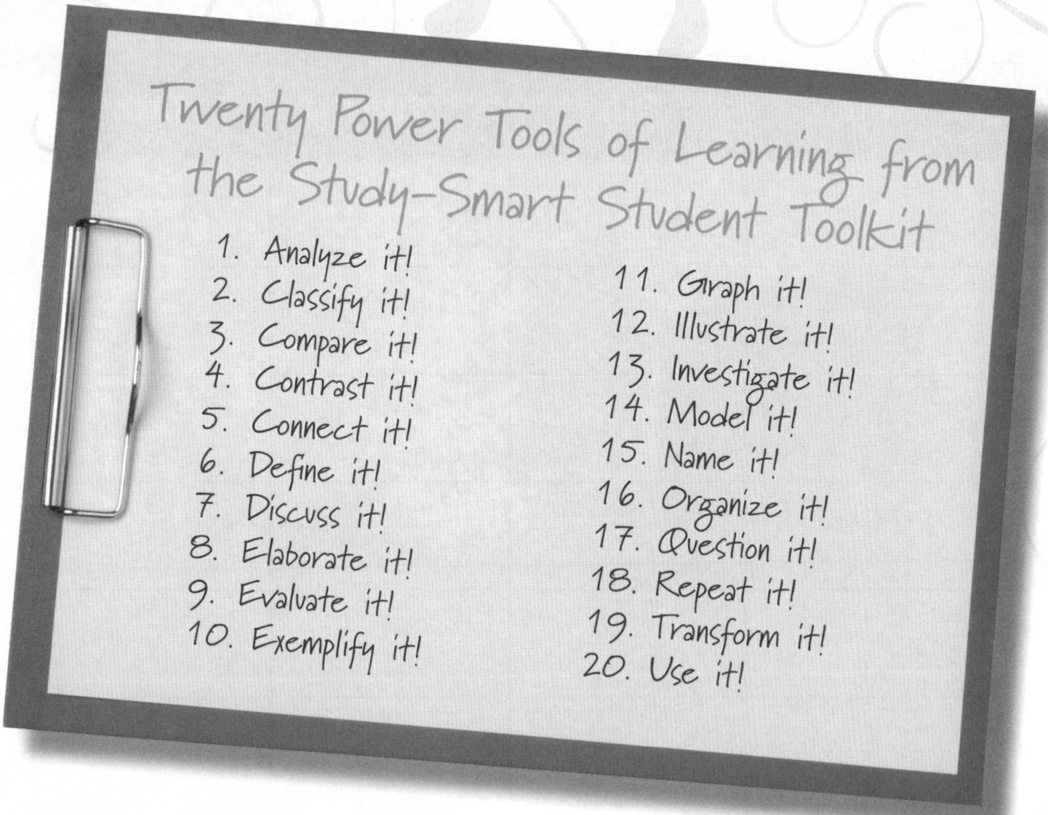
Twenty Power Tools of Learning from the Study-Smart Student Toolkit
1. Analyze it!
2. Classify it!
3. Compare it!
4. Contrast it!
5. Connect it!
6. Define it!
7. Discuss it!
8. Elaborate it!
9. Evaluate it!
10. Exemplify it!
11. Graph it!
12. Illustrate it!
13. Investigate it!
14. Model it!
15. Name it!
16. Organize it!
17. Question it!
18. Repeat it!
19. Transform it!
20. Use it!

Parents' Guide to the Study-Smart Student Toolkit

What's the difference between an expert learner and one who struggles to process new information? The study-smart student employs learning strategies that I call the Power Tools of Learning. When students use the tools shown on the chart above, many different parts of the brain fire up and come online. And when students are both cognitively and emotionally engaged in what they are learning, they process information more effectively and at a deeper level and can later recall more details of what they've learned.

Our job as parents is to create an environment that allows our students the time and opportunity to use these power tools. Here's how:

- ✔ Focus on the three P's—Projects, Papers, and Performances. These types of activities (as opposed to rote memorization, for example) require kids to organize their time, think through multiple aspects of an assignment, and stay focused on the material over several days or even weeks. This approach fosters total immersion in the new information, and that's when deep processing occurs.
- ✔ Trigger positive emotions. We learn more when we are laughing, happy, experiencing pleasure, or lost in awe and wonder. Curl up on the couch together daily and read aloud. Integrate learning into the relational moments of your family life such as dinner time, vacations, and extended family visits.
- ✔ Build leisure into the school day. While we are at rest, our brains continue to process and store information recently learned. Teach your children to value daydreaming, chasing after rabbit trails, playing outdoors, and watching clouds. A good motto to adopt is "Rigor and rest, rigor and rest." By supplying each in equal parts, your kids will prosper.

Yes, these strategies do require more time than simple memorization. But this is the stuff of deep cognition, and the process cannot be rushed. However, you will find you pick up speed over time for two reasons: First, your children will understand more fully what they have already learned, so re-teaching and reviewing will not be necessary. Secondly, your children will find they love to learn, and this motivation will transform them into independent and lifelong learners, making your job much easier.

Download the full article for the Study-Smart Student Toolkit at DebraBell.com.

Student This planning guide will help you and your teen map out the high school years.
See chapter 12 of *The Ultimate Guide to Homeschooling Teens* for more information.

		8th	9th	10th	11th	12th
MATH	Semester 1					
	Semester 2					
ENGLISH	Semester 1					
	Semester 2					
SOCIAL STUDIES	Semester 1					
	Semester 2					
SCIENCE	Semester 1					
	Semester 2					
LANGUAGE	Semester 1					
	Semester 2					
ELECTIVES/ OTHER	Semester 1					
	Semester 2					
TESTS	Semester 1					
	Semester 2					
SUMMER						

Student Below is a sample for a competitive merit scholarship candidate.

	8th	9th	10th	11th	12th
MATH	Algebra 1	Algebra 2	Geometry	Pre-Calculus	AP Calculus AB
	Math Counts	SAT Math Review	Trigonometry	SAT Math Review	
ENGLISH	Intro to Composition	American Literature	English Literature	AP Language	AP Literature
	Intro to Poetry	Advanced Composition	Shakespeare		
SOCIAL STUDIES	World Cultures	State History	AP U.S. History	AP European History	Church History
		U.S. Government			
SCIENCE	Physical Science	Biology	Chemistry	Physics	Advanced Chemistry
LANGUAGE	Spanish 1	Spanish 2	Spanish 3	Spanish 4	AP Spanish
			at community college	at community college	
ELECTIVES/ OTHER	Music	Music	Music Theory	Music Recital	Music
			Internship	College Visits	College Applications
TESTS			AP	PSAT SAT I	SAT I
			AP History	AP Euro / AP Language	AP Spanish / AP Lit / AP Calculus
SUMMER			Missions Trip	Missions Trip	

Year-End Review

Summarize the progress made by each child and the degree to which beginning-of-the-year goals were reached. Give God glory for prayers answered and evidence of growth in your children spiritually, academically, and emotionally.

Year-End Review

Summarize the progress made by each child and the degree to which beginning-of-the-year goals were reached. Give God glory for prayers answered and evidence of growth in your children spiritually, academically, and emotionally.

Notes

Bibliography

Adeney, Miriam. *A Time for Risking: Priorities for Women.* Vancouver: Regent College Publishing, 1987.

Augustine. *The Confessions*. New York: Clark, 1876.

Bennett, Arthur G. *The Valley of Vision: A Collection of Puritan Prayers & Devotions*. Carlisle, PA: Banner of Truth, 2003.

Bonhoeffer, Dietrich. *Life Together: The Classic Exploration of Christian Community*. New York: Harper Collins, 1978.

Carmichael, Amy. *Gold Chord: The Story of a Fellowship.* London: Society for Promoting Christian Knowledge, 1952.

Chesterton, Gilbert Keith. *A Miscellany of Men*. New York: Dodd, Mead, 1912.

—— *The Collected Works of G. K. Chesterton*. San Francisco: Ignatius Press, 2005.

—— *Orthodoxy.* London: John Lane Company, 1909.

Cowman, Mrs. Charles E. *Streams in the Desert*. Grand Rapids: Zondervan, 1997.

Donne, John. "Holy Sonnets XIV." *The Works of the English Poets, from Chaucer to Cowper.* Ed. Alexander Chalmers. London: J. Johnson 1810. 198.

Dostoyevsky, Fyodor. *The Brothers Karamazov.* New York: Macmillan, 1922.

Draper, Edythe. *Draper's Book of Quotations for the Christian World*. Carol Stream: Tyndale House, 1992.

Elliot, Elizabeth. *Let Me Be a Woman*. Carol Stream: Tyndale House, 1976.

France, Anatole. *Thais.* MobileReference.

George, Elizabeth. *Following God with All Your Heart*. Irvine: Harvest House, 2008.

Greene, Graham. *The Power and the Glory*. New York: Viking Press, 1951.

Hayford, Jack. *31 Days Meditating on the Majesty of Jesus*. Carol Stream: Tyndale House, 2007.

Herbert, George. "Providence" *Sacred Poetry*. Ed. Henry Stebbing. London: J. F. Dove 1832.

Holt, John. *Teach Your Own*. New York: Delacorte Press, 1981.

Hopkins, Gerard Manley. "God's Grandeur." *God's Grandeur and Other Poems*. Mineola: Courier Dover Publications, 1995.

—— "Pied Beauty" *Hopkins re-constructed.* Ed. Justus George Lawler. New York: Continuum International Publishing Group, 2000.

Jay, William. *Prayers for the Use of Families.* Boston: Henry Whipple, 1821.

Kennedy, G. Geoffrey Anketell Sutddert. *The Wicked Gate*; or *Plain Bread*. London: Hodder and Stoughton, 1923.

Law, Henry. *Family Prayers for Four Weeks*. London: James Nisbet & Co., 1868.

Law, William. *A Serious Call to a Devout and Holy Life.* Boston: W. Baynes, 1797.

Lear, Linda. *Beatrix Potter: A Life in Nature.* New York: Macmillan, 2008.

Lewis, Clives Staples and Clyde Kilby. *A Mind Awake: An Anthology of C. S. Lewis.* Boston: Houghton Mifflin Harcourt, 2003.

—— *Collected Letters: Narnia*, Cambridge and Joy 1950-1963. Nashville: Harper Collins, 2006.

—— *God in the Dock*. Grand Rapids: Eerdmans, 1970.

Lubac, Henri de. *Paradoxes of Faith*. San Francisco: Ignatius Press, 1987.

Macaulay, Susan Schaeffer. *For the Family's Sake*. Wheaton: Crossway, 1999.

Manser, Martin H. ed., *The Westminster Collection of Christian Quotations.* Louisville: Westminster John Knox Press, 2001.

Marshall, Catherine. *A Man Called Peter*. Ada: Chosen Books, 2002.

—— *Adventures in Prayer*. New York: F. H. Revell, 1976.

—— *Christy*. Grand Rapids: Zondervan, 1967.

Mason, Charlotte. *Home Education*. London: K. Paul, Trench, Trübner, 1906.

—— *School Education*. Carol Stream: Tyndale House, 1907.

—— *Original Homeschooling Series Volume 3*. Carol Stream: Tyndale House, 1989.

Moore, Beth. *Further Still: A Collection of Poetry and Vignettes*. Nashville: B&H Publishing Group, 2004.

—— *Praying God's Word*. Nashville: B&H Publishing Group, 2009.

Pascal, Blaise. *Pensées*. New York: Guillaume Desprez, 1670.

Peter, Laurence J. *Peter's Quotations*. NY: Morrow, 1977.

Piper, John. *Don't Waste Your Life.* Wheaton: Crossway Books, 2004.

—— *Future Grace*. New York: Random House, 2005.

—— *The Pleasures of God.* New York: Random House, 2000.

—— *Seeing and Savoring Jesus Christ*. Wheaton: Crossway Books, 2004.

Ryle, John Charles. *Wheat or Chaff?* New York: R. Carter, 1853.

St. Peter, Anthony. *The Greatest Quotations of All-Time*. Xlibris, 2010.

Smith, Hannah Whitall. *The Christian's Secret of a Happy Life.* Ada: Revell, 1888.

Spurgeon, Charles Haddon. "The Bed and Its Covering," *The Spurgeon Archive*, Sermon #244, http://www.spurgeon.org/sermons/0244.htm

—— *C. H. Spurgeon's Autobiography*. New York: Passmore and Alabaster, 1900.

—— *Illustrations and Meditations*. New York: Funk and Wagnalls, 1883.

—— *Morning by Morning.* New York: Sheldon and Company, 1866.

—— *Spurgeon on Prayer.* Alachua, FL: Bridge Logos Foundation, 2009.

Swindoll, Charles R. *Man to Man*. Grand Rapids: Zondervan, 1998.

Tozer, Aiden Wilson. *The Pursuit of God*. New York: Christian Publications, 1996.

Trelease, Jim. *The New Read-Aloud Handbook*. New York: Penguin Books, 1989.

Watts, Isaac. "Felicity Above." *The Works of the English Poets, from Chaucer to Cowper*. Ed. Alexander Chalmers. London: J. Johnson, 1810. 22.

About Debra Bell

Debra Bell, PhD, is the best-selling author of the award-winning *The Ultimate Guide to Homeschooling, The Ultimate Guide to Homeschooling Teens*, and the Ultimate Planners for moms, teens, and students. Currently, she is completing *Writers in Residence* and *Readers in Residence*–a multivolume language arts program for grades 4 and up.

A former high school and college English teacher, Debra and her husband Kermit home educated their four kids from kindergarten through high school graduation. During her homeschooling years, Debra founded three homeschool co-ops, which continue today. Her articles on homeschooling have appeared in many publications, including *The Old Schoolhouse Magazine, Homeschooling Today, The Home School Court Report,* and *Thriving Families Magazine*. She has been a keynote or featured speaker at national and international venues for more than twenty years. Debra currently serves as vice-chair of the Global Home Education Exchange Council and chair of the research committee. She coedited the *Journal of School Choice* special issue on home education research (September 2016, Vol. 10, No. 3) and *Homeschooling in the 21st Century: Research and Prospect*, published by Routledge.

Debra holds a bachelor's degree in communications education, a master's in English, and a doctorate in educational psychology. A pioneer in online education, Debra is also executive director of Aim Academy, which provides online college prep and AP® courses for grades 7-12, both stateside and abroad. For more information about her online classes, books, curriculum, and speaking schedule, visit **DebraBell.com.**